ALSO BY EDWARD C. LARSON

Leaves

from the
autumns of yesterday

a collection by

EDWARD C. LARSON

fly by night graphics
santa cruz • california

Cover: Cedar elm (*Ulmus crassifolia*) styled by Greg Setter.

Back cover photo: *Edward C. Larson* by Patricia D. Richards.

Cover and book design: Sheila Setter.

Grateful acknowledgment is made for permission to use:
  Grandpa's Barn II, copyright © 2000 by Patricia D.
Richards. All rights reserved.
  The Fishtail General Store, *Grandpa's Barn*, and *Along the
Stillwater*, copyright © 1992 by Patricia D. Richards.
All rights reserved.

Work by Mr. Larson previously published includes:
  "Walton Light — Santa Cruz Harbor" published in the
Santa Cruz Sentinel, 2017.
  "Arana Gulch" published in *Seabright News*, 2017.
  "Sixty-Fathom Line" reprinted from *Pebbles from a
Favored Shore*, 2005.
  "Night Flight" reprinted from *Gaff-Rigged Remembrance*,
2000.
  "Charlie's Wintertime" published in *Junior College
Magazine*, 1991.
  "Narrow Paths" and "Last Night" reprinted from
Some Things We Lived With, 1972.

Published by Fly by Night Graphics.

Address inquiries to the publisher or author at
publisher@journey2astar.net
www.journey2astar.net

ISBN: 978-0-9654376-3-9
Printed in the United States of America.

Each of us
must know those times
when our souls are filled
with the specters of grief and sorrow
that darken the heart.

When no sun lights my pathway,
I promise you,
I shall remember this:
Mourning is simply the price we pay
for the privilege of loving
those we have gathered
in to our very beings.

I shall never forego that joy of loving others
to escape the pain
of falling tears.

- Edward C. Larson -

contents

II

III

IV

LEAVES
from the
Autumns of Yesterday

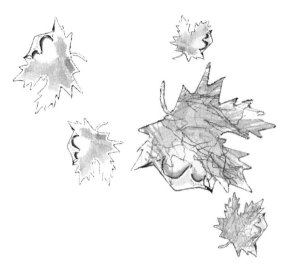

Maple Leaves - Edward C. Larson, 2017

author's note

I am thrilled to have lived the countless moments of this life. Passing seasons filled with joy, sorrow, passion, and adventure have been draped across my shoulders by the hands of fate and circumstance. Their grasp has reached out to me from some far place—beyond an endless void, which I shall never know nor even contemplate. In a ceaseless metaphor, the bright-hued leaves of good fortune have littered my aimless pathway through every season and peril my years have left behind.

I recall a maple tree I used to call my own, even though it was in Mr. Gates's backyard. It was a favorite haunt in my early childhood years. I climbed it only when Southwesterlies really roared their loudest about our home on Phinney Ridge. It was then that I sought the highest and most tenuous of branches to truly be one with the wind and flying leaves.

It was perhaps there, in the highest branches, that my metaphor of living took root in a child's mind intent on trying to understand it all.

My years have been borne in the endless wonder of blowing winds, the highest branches, and the beauty of falling leaves.

I can only wish the same for you.

|

Days decrease,
And autumn grows,
Autumn is everything.
- *Robert Browning*

Rusted Plow - Edward C. Larson, 2017

rusted plow

As we both grew older and I reached the age where his words had true meaning for me, he spoke often of the land and his love for the valley and the river. I know now that he waited through the child years until I was old enough to understand that which he wished to share. When he spoke of Montana, there was a quiet vastness in his voice—echoing the remembrance of the plains and the mountains and their blessed emptiness…as if there were never a need for people, only the adventure of a new and unsullied space.

He spoke of land and sky, not as entities or separate things but as parts of a whole, like what I imagined a Native American Indian might say, imparting a spiritual reality to the air he breathed and to the ground on which he stood.

I had to *hear* this *feeling* again.

On a Wednesday, on a borrowed horse, I climbed the Madison Ridge, turned west, and rode until the ranch and valley disappeared, seeking that sense of aloneness he had made the child understand. Some miles of short prairie grass lay behind us when, about noon, I came upon a broken plow that had rusted in that quiet place—perhaps since before I was born. The mare grazed easy, and I sat for some time looking back from whence I had come.

I had noticed a red-tailed hawk circling miles back; now there were no birds to be seen. A slight wind moved across the brown stubble, its whisper the only sound in this universe. Save for the intrusion of a moldering log shack far to the south, this vista had not changed for ten thousand years. I imagined a small Crow band on coarse horses pausing here a century before, seeing what I saw, then moving on to the east in search of a different tomorrow.

The dun hills, randomly stocked with low pine and live oak, rose in stairsteps toward a sky that he had known and told me of: a single immensity crowning this prairie.

This was *his* place and *his* solitude, and it had been his gift to tell me of it so I could sense it and seek it as he had.

I was loath to leave.

For some little time, we had shared each other again…as if there had been two horses, side by each in the afternoon's grassy warmth…

and we spoke of snaffle bits,
and saddle guns,
and bummer lambs,
and stars.

Campbell's Soup Can - Edward C. Larson, 2017

remembrance

Memories.
Thrown against the misted walls
of hours and days gone by.
Laughter and childhood.
Swirling out beyond the dreams I owned,
leaping in quantum speed toward the void,
the richness receding,
moment by moment,
into a place beyond recall...
into some black star very old,
vanishing into the cold emptiness of being forgotten.

And lost.
Far beyond the grasp of years'-gnarled hands to hold.
Worn fingers.
Dry and rasping.
Grasping.
Reaching to embrace what was,
to hold and mold into shapes
the gentle forms that might have been...
but somehow never could become.
And never will.

And moments.
Hiding in torn bindings.
Pressed between the yellowed pages of the past,
authored and proofed
and irretrievably returned to an archive
somewhere out there.
Beyond sight.
And sound.

Past laughter.
And the lovely songs that were,
floating slowly by like wheat straws...
caught and turning for a moment
in the eddies of my mind,
just beyond my reach to hold.
Quite like the golden ring I nearly caught,
but I was listening much too closely
to the music...
as the carousel whirled swiftly by.

Arana Gulch Barn - Edward C. Larson, 2017

arana gulch

The wind is only slightly from the west…a small breeze
of no consequence. Walking is easy; and the pathway,
hard-packed, leads gently down the sloping fields of
Arana Gulch. The yellow ball of sun is not quite down,
and there's enough shine left to brush the meadow
grasses with gold and light the Eucs along the harbor's
east side. Their trunks are orange-yellow in the sinking
light, and the brilliant green of their tops is as rich as
green ever gets. Eucalyptus trees have always seemed
bizarre to me — I mean, like they didn't put their clothes
on until they were half grown—thus, the naked,
shedding trunks and foliage only high, high up.

A fine home for blue herons, but all in all, a strange kind of tree. Imagine putting on leaves only as an afterthought!

To my left, the meadow slants quickly into a deep *barranca*. A little creek, wild with willows, runs at its bottom. God knows what's down there. I won't go that way. It's become darkened there, shaded from the sinking light, and the deep gully's hues have turned from warm to the cold grays and blues that speak of night and real darkness. This is a "silent-y" place. Not threatening. Simply very still, with blackberry vines but very few birds. It is a place for "walking thoughts"; and quite often, those are the best kind.

I'm sure you know Arana Gulch climbs like a red-tailed hawk all the way to Chaminade and De Laveaga. It was once a *whole thing* — pristine, large, and alone — but now it's bisected by Soquel Avenue and Highway One and *God knows* what else. Where I am now is the best part — this lovely meadow above the harbor that at this moment turns into evening. The pollution of traffic noise has been blissfully erased by time and distance. In these last minutes, I've walked from Soquel Avenue with its Foster Freeze and used-car sales hype into a blessed aloneness.

In my reverie, José Arana, the namesake of this place, stands beside me in this very spot; the year is 1833. Sunburned and squinty-eyed, he looks over his newly secured *rancho*, which, in the years ahead, will feed his family and kill his child. His adobe home is on the bluff that will one day cradle Holy Cross Cemetery.

José Arana is now gone more than a century and a half. And slowly, what remains of his land is being squeezed in by houses that, like the proverbial camel, "stick their noses under the tent." And in so doing, consume all that is open and free.

I believe the small segment bounded by my evening footsteps holds perhaps all that remains of the man and the memory-threads he created to tie us to the past.

There is a certain sadness here, a clinging reticence to let go the drama and pathos of the interminable years between us. Only the rains and the sun's ceaseless metronome remain unchanged.

Our time in this place was determined by the stars.

If he can hear my whispered voice across the years, I wish him well.

Santa Cruz Tarplant - Edward C. Larson, 2000

narrow paths

To most, I would suppose,
a field
at any time of day
might seem a simple, mundane thing to see.
"It's earth and grass and not much else,"
a passerby might say, or...
"I will stop some other time or some less busy day."

For, after all, a field's just common land.
There is no treasure trove hidden from our sight—
for prying eye to search,
or curious hand to steal
from out this pauper earth this night.

But may I tell you of the many things I've found?
(I've promised myself this visit for a month...
or maybe two.)
The smell,
the feel,
the pleasant warmth upon this ground.
The evening light.
The coming night.
For what I've found could be of interest to you.

I found, as well you might,
a man
content to be alone,
enraptured still by childhood's simple joys:
the flight of birds—
not noticed much since I have grown—
and other things I found I had not known—
the strange delight
and mystery
of some unfamiliar noise.

To see with child's excitement
flowers
never viewed before.
(How many myriad things must fall my lot to fail to see
for only want of time
to make the quest to learn this lore?)
Of simple things—
like hills, and fields of narrow paths,
and teeming shores—
till yet, with failing eyes and trembling hands,
another land presents itself to me.

I found a growing weed I hadn't ever known at all.
And some remembered still
from days so long ago at play.
And felt again across an older, coarser face and arms,
the night breeze calls
an end to all
the richness of this quite unusual day.

But it is growing dark...
and as the shadows of the night grow long,
I leave now
as the sun deserts the sky.
And someday, if it strikes your mood,
I'll let you come along.
Perhaps among the grasses of this summer-scented field,
you'll find besides these things
yourself,
if you are half so fortunate as I.

Dry Camp at Granite Peak - Edward C. Larson, 2017

winter meat

For three years, Charlie's being had been hardened by an anvil of work and winter. His arms were linear and dense as cordwood with skin crisscrossed by scars of barbwire and buck brush. The seasons had coarsened his hands and face, and there was nothing of a town or city left inside him. It was as if he had donned his Montana valley like a pelt and had thus become one of its creatures.

In the pervasive solitude of his life, he existed now as part predator, led by a primal logic: sensing, smelling, knowing, and embracing this special, chosen place. The years had dealt fairly with him. There were now a few steers bearing his *Hanging Y Quarter Circle* brand and a small band of sheep whose brash mouthings broke the valley's silence all too often; and he had assembled about him a flock of stringy chickens of dubious ancestry and one large, cotton-eyed sheepdog named simply, Joshua.

The log and sod shed on which he had labored so long was little more than shelter...only a mound, in fact, set some little distance above the river's high-water mark. It had warmed and served him since the beginning; and for now, it was enough. In July, he had hauled three wagonloads of lumber down from the mill at Big Timber. Somewhere in the days ahead, there would be time for house building and the attendant dangers and hardships of laboring alone.

August and early September passed innocently enough. Toward the end of September's third week, however, he caught himself looking often at the sky. Like a stone in his shoe, there was the soft insistence of coming winter, a seeming need to prepare.

He did not ignore it.

At dawn on a Tuesday, he loaded a packhorse called Roxi and saddled Maude, his roan mare. She was a good mount, but oft times displayed an independence he didn't admire. Kneeing her belly to draw the cinch tight, he saw the beginning of winter hair cropping from her withers and chest. He reckoned she'd need it soon enough.

Satisfied that the stove fire was dying, he drove two nails into the jamb to secure the cabin door, walked to the horses, and slid the Winchester into a leather saddle scabbard that the years had molded to fit its precise form. It seemed things were ready. As he swung into the saddle, the horse, rank from nonriding, jumped sideways, twisting to bite him. With a loud, "*God damn you!*" Charlie lashed the heavy reins across her head. Their differences settled in Charlie's favor, they rode slowly toward the south, the packhorse on a slack lead plodding along like some living afterthought.

He passed through the village of Fishtail, waving briefly at brothers Henry and Vince Evans, who were drinking early on a saloon porch still covered with white dew. The sun had risen slowly and yellow-red and would grant some slight warmth through the day as he continued south across a dry prairie tufted with buffalo grass and tumbleweed.

In the afternoon, he spotted a band of pronghorn antelope foraging warily on a rise to the west; at near dark, there was the panicked crashing of some creature in a *barranca* close by. Other than that, he'd seen nothing. That night, there was a slim fare of beans, jerky, boiled coffee, and a twig fire offering no warmth and little light against a darkness that spoke of the cold to come.

By Wednesday midmorning, they had begun climbing slowly through the tamarack and lodgepole pine that skirted the knees of Granite Peak, highest of the

Absaroka Mountains. Charlie dismounted to rest the horses for a short while and studied the vast aloneness of his world.

The sky and earth spoke of early snow. The knee-high grass in which he stood stretched dry and brittle across the meadow below the timberline, bending awkwardly in the persistent chill wind from the northeast. High up, a large flock of geese out of the north-Canada tundra was heading south along the flyway.

It seemed early for that.

In the afternoon, far down the mountain, he saw a group of six Crow braves. They were poorly mounted, one with a travois that drew tired parallels in the sandy soil. Heads down and dispirited, they had joined the migration of their fellow creatures.

He dismounted quickly and held the mare's nose to suppress a whinny. At times, it was wise to be silent. Almost painfully, the Indians made their way south and east, driven by some timeless intuition toward a place of wintering in this land that had once belonged to them. They passed totally unaware of Charlie's presence on the rock face above.

Toward sundown, he picked his way across a large field of granite rubble sloping down from a stand of whitebark pine. There was still a little warmth, and he was tired and close to saddle sleeping. Just as his nodding head began to fall, the wild huckleberry a hundred yards up the slope exploded with noise and commotion. He grabbed the saddle horn as the mare arched in terror, jerking the packhorse to its knees on the rocks. There was a glimpse of the monstrous brown back and the sound of the loud, guttural *whuff whuff* as the grizzly and her two cubs charged upslope and vanished in the timber.

He had come too close to being thrown.

He dozed no more.

Sleeping lightly that night beside a small fire, Charlie kept his saddle gun close at hand. Next morning, in a nearby meadow, he shot a large buck, skinned it, and left the gut pile steaming in the open grass for easy finding. Time and food were short now for the sow and her cubs. By the feel and smell of the cold morning wind, they would be going to den soon.

At midmorning, frost remained on the shaded brown grass, and the horse's breath was still fog. He loaded and tied the mule deer carcass on the pack animal, turned, and headed back whence he came, unnoticed and dwarfed but fulfilled by the immensity of the high meadows he had grown to love.

The breath of coming winter followed him down the foothills and across the flats. He rode into Fishtail on Saturday afternoon, cold and chewing on a piece of elk jerky he had stowed in a medicine bag tied to the saddle cantle. Looping the reins around a splintered hitching rack, he walked through the unpainted door of the Carbon Saloon and bought a pint of whiskey. Not wanting to linger, he spoke briefly with Andrew Johnson, waved to a table of stud players, and then remounted and headed north.

By seven o'clock, he would be home.

When he topped the last rise to gaze down on the valley of the Stillwater, the bottle was half gone and stowed in a saddlebag. The river had picked up the blue-violet of last light, and the willows had turned black with shadow.

He reined in and stopped.

Maude, sensing hay, fought the bit and stomped with impatience while the pack animal's head arched low in silent resignation.

Charlie turned in the saddle to sweep the scene around him.

It was very cold now, and the windblown clouds were clogging the sky with the portent of certain snow.

From far down the draw, there was the cry of a nighthawk, then only the immense quiet and treasure of aloneness that had become food and drink for his body and mind.

He clucked gently to the mare and rode slowly downward toward the log shack, lost now in the evening's deepening darkness.

No matter.

The trilogy of man and beasts had already been branded forever as creatures of this living land and sky. Together, they read the scent of "home hay" carried on the edge of the freezing breeze.

Their journey had ended.

Old Seattle Streetcar - Edward C. Larson, 2017

corduroy pants

I remember streetcars in the rain,
    great colored bugs
    with trolleys like sparklers and screeching wheels.

Gram would take me downtown on Number 21,
    orange and green
    with white window trim.

And once, she took me to the Browning-King store,
    where they gave you models of planes and boats
    if you bought clothes there.
    She bought me my first pair of corduroy pants.
    I got the *Bounty.*

I remember the thin salesman in the brown suit
    with threads showing through
    on the sleeves and cuffs.

It was the Depression;
    and Gram had put pennies and nickels
    in a ginger jar;
    and when she had enough saved,
    she'd buy stuff for Charlie and me.
    Like clothes.

I remember walking around the store
    feeling the *zzz, zzz, zzz* sound
    when the pant legs rubbed together
    and liking that even better
    than the *Bounty* that was free
    and came with a big colored box
    with balsa wood and glue
    and plans I was too anxious to follow.

Later, when it was real dark and rainy,
    we took the streetcar home to Phinney Ridge;
    we lived in a nice house that Pop built...
    till the goddamn mortgage company took it away.

It was so late, there was only Gram and me.

The motorman sat in the dark
    behind a gray curtain with little green moons on it
    where he moved levers and stuff
    to make the cable car go
    and stepped on a big bell that he used
    to get people and automobiles out of the way.

We sat in the lighted part,
    on caned seats with brass handles on the ends
    that were always polished
    from people grabbing them.

And I remember watching the leather straps
    that people hung on to
    swing back and forth,
    back and forth;
    they were smooth and black from hands.

And when you pulled the rope, the cable car stopped—
    always at the next corner.

The streetcar didn't go close to our house,
    and Gram walked slow.
    Like always, I held her hand
    and stepped from square to square;
    you know,
    "Step on a crack—break your mother's back!"

We walked past Woodland Park
    with wet bears inside
    and past the church where Catholics went.

Gram said they were strange people—
    not like us;
    but I loved Mildred Novak in the fourth grade,
    and she went there.

Past Piggly Wiggly and Bilan's Drug Store,
    where Charlie played the pinball machine—
    he had learned how to tilt it and still win
    and get us nickels for the movie.

By the time we got home, the rain had stopped,
    and the sidewalks weren't mirrors
    under the street lights anymore.
    It was hard to see where the cracks and lines were,
    so I just walked regular.

I wore the corduroy pants for a long time...
    till the knee patches wore out from playing mibs,
    and they were too short for me.

They never sounded as good again
    like they did in the store.

I guess the rain washed out the *zzz, zzz, zzz* sound.

Charlie was older than me;
    he laughed at the *Bounty* after I finished it,
    but I had a lot of fun gluing it together.

It didn't sail worth a damn in the frog pond
    behind Binyon's place;
    but it looked OK to me,
    almost like the picture on the box.

Montana Shack - Edward C. Larson, 2017

charlie's wintertime

By midmorning Thursday, the sky was crossed with mare's tail clouds. Precursors to the coming storm. He had forked extra hay into the corral for the roan mare, Maude, and his packhorse, Roxi. They were "easy keepers," fat and covered with an extra heavy coat of coarse winter hair.

The shaggy cattle were scattered—some in the draw and a few high on the grade, dark umber forms against the gray lowering sky. Better than three cords of dry cottonwood and alder were laid close by the cabin door; and Josh, the dog, was "sticky," crowding his master's footsteps.

Charlie and his beasts had done all they could to prepare.

By three in the afternoon, with a gentle, soft beginning, the snow began to fall.

Two hours later, the "blue norther" wind arrived, angling the falling snow and whistling with a low moan against the cabin corners. Then came the cold and darkness, creeping on all fours over the grade and down into the river valley. The cattle, seeking each other's heat, came together in silent resignation, while the river lowered its voice and its edges turned to glass. The thin wisp of wood smoke from the cabin rode the wind toward the south, knowing the worst was yet to come.

Through the night, Charlie shivered in his bed beneath a heavy robe. The small stove warmed only itself, its rosy promise futile against the mounting cold inside. The tiny cabin, savaged by the rising wind, offered no comfort, only bare survival for the dog and his master. By three in the morning, water in the wooden bucket had frozen solid, extending above the rim in a crooked column of icy hardness.

Abandoning hope for sleep that never came, Charlie rose at six o'clock that morning and walked to the window. Scratching a hole in the frosted surface, he looked out. Beyond the frozen window sill, there was only silence and a world of white swirling snow.

Beside that…nothing.

The dog at his feet whimpered lowly, wanting warmth.

After four days, Charlie was certain there would be no heat on the earth again…forever. The snow lay two feet deep on the flat around the cabin, and it was a struggle to reach the pole corral to feed the horses. The wind rose and fell, moaning and screeching against the cabin logs. The "norther" was a presence, an unwelcome guest who arrived uninvited, talked too much, and stayed too long.

Imprisoned in a world of his own choosing, Charlie moved mechanically through a cold existence, using his instincts to survive and sharing that primitive commitment with his dog. His beasts wandered somewhere in the white world beyond his vision and beyond his care. He was a lamed shepherd, without a crook, without a fold, and lost in a hostile white land.

On the evening of the fifth day, Charlie sensed a change. It was not a warming, surely, but a difference in the icy prison that surrounded him. Followed by the dog, he stepped out through the cabin door, walked a few paces, looked about, and was staggered by the beauty of the night as sharp-edged as flint.

The moon was nearly full and brushed the frozen snow with an exquisite blue he had never seen before. The sky was cloudless, and the granite tops of the Beartooth Range to the south seemed only an arm's length away. Halfway up the grade, on a high ridge purged of snow, a few of his steers grazed, their backs dusted white. The cottonwood and willow in the draw had been painted with ice and stood like bone lace against the blackness of a sky dotted with countless stars.

Nothing moved.

The grazing cattle seemed frozen in time.

The Stillwater River, shining like some great angular mirror, doubled in an ice-blue encore the image of the trees along its banks.

Even the dog beside him seemed transfixed by the glory of the night.

The breath of man and animal, co-survivors of the storm, blended together in a small cloud that hung suspended in the pervasive cold.

And over all, in this fragile vastness that belonged to him, there was that primal silence that impacted his being: the joy of the land in which nothing was worn, nothing used, a universe of stillness in which one could easily hear the beating of his own heart.

Patting Josh, he turned back toward the cabin door and the faint warmth within, realizing with a start that he would be forever different from the man who had first arrived here.

1934

Lest we forget, even for a moment,
this is from whence we came.
This is the genesis of the Dutch Colonial
at 203 North 65th.

Our grandpa built it with two bare hands,
a hammer,
and a handsaw.
Once bright and shiny new,
here, it had fallen on hard times
and a decade of wanting, as had we.

It was a home filled with the warmth of love,
and a sawdust burner,
which chased away the cold of morning rains.

We lost it in '34 to a goddamn mortgage company,
for the want of a few hundred dollars.
It was one of the few times I saw Gram cry.

My dearest family,
look well about this picture.
It smacks of the lens of Dorothea Lange
and the agony of those worse off than we.
The tattered backstairs wanted repairs badly,
but we owed two hundred dollars
to Mr. Ries at the grocery store,
and there was no money for the treads and risers.

Too, there was a nobility about their splintered surface,
a deep and abiding kindness
we must all remember:
Gram fed the passing "down and outers"
on those stairs—
men seeking the dignity of work,
and finding nothing in their days
but the endless chain
of hardscrabble disappointment.
They always left a "thanks"
and an empty plate filled with deepest gratitude
before departing,
shutting the sagging gate of compassion
quietly behind them.

Grandpa Charlie, Eddie Boy, Gram, and Mom - from the Author's Collection

I would hope that you see here in our faces
not only the façade of want,
but also resolution
and the wondrous anticipation of something better,
of something brighter,
and of the small triumph
of passing through tattered times
and reaching out, as did we,
toward the aura of a fine tomorrow.

These, then, are the people who saw me through,
sparing me from the worst,
while nailing together the studs and headers
that have formed the "self"
I live in.

They stand behind me in quiet dignity
and have given to me—and you—
the gift of the golden key to the door
of what we were
and who we are.

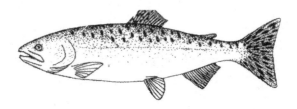

Trout - Edward C. Larson, 2005

wolf river

It was '34 when he took us back to Montana…the first time I was to be there. The Depression had robbed us of everything else, and when they foreclosed on the goddamn mortgage, the only thing left for him was to return to the valley for renewal.

I was nine when he took me out along the Stillwater.

We took a fly rod, some sandwiches, and an old Winchester .30-30.

I think we walked about a mile or so…there were large boulders and the carcasses of cottonwood downed by winter winds.

The water was flawless.

Crystalline.

The clearest I've known, and filled with trout shadows and bottomed with beautiful colored stones.

We sat and ate for some short time; then he walked a hundred yards away and stuck his straw hat on the top of a downed cottonwood that was shaded by a few green willows. When he came back, he loaded the rifle and levered a cartridge into the chamber. I remember him smiling and saying, "Watch this, Eddie Boy!"

The shot rang out, and the echo slammed back from across the river. When I ran to get the hat, it lay on the far side of the cottonwood with a neat hole right through the headband.

We took turns; and when we were out of shells, there were four holes in the hat...one of them mine — at least so he said.

I caught four trout that afternoon.

It was "catch and release 'em" because the Madisons had planned a chicken dinner that night.

Although I would have liked to take them back and show them to Gram, there was a small sort of joy watching them swim away.

"Besides," he said, "she'd seen lots of trout before."

On the way home, he told me he had shot a wolf back there where we had lunch.

It had been thirty years before in the dead of winter.

He was a cowboy then.

The wolf had killed three of his sheep, and there was blood all over the snow.

I asked him how many shots it took.

"Just one, Eddie Boy," he said.

"Just one."

Rooftop and Chimney Study - Edward C. Larson, 1984

hard freeze

The near of you
dawned yesterday
on smoked wind.

Late last night, you crossed the upper meadow
where the fence is down,
making passage easy.

I saw your steps in crushed frost
close by where the summer apple tree lays dead
and fallow black,
arms pinioned by the cold.

Winter - Edward C. Larson, 2017

the lane is black-iced ditch to ditch...

I wish you had let me know that you'd be here
(hell, there's a phone out front of Withon's store),
or stuck a cardboard note beneath the left-hand wiper
of my Chevy truck.

I'd have seen it going after morning mash.

Instead, you come onto my place
expecting a handshake—
or something more—
for making the dog's breath clouds,
and laying window glass neatly on the crick
even in the widest places,
and making fence wire
snap, snap
and pull the staples out.

Axes,
lean barn-side,
splintered by your close
with slivers that hole five-dollar gloves—
yet, there's a small fear shared across the hearth
with the last of the embers:
Have I laid by enough alder?

The right rear tire's smooth,
and the lane is black-iced ditch to ditch.
No chance to run away.

I'm not surprised you're here.

I saw your steps in crushed frost
high in the upper meadow
close by where the summer apple tree lays dead
and fallow black,
arms pinioned by your cold.

Grandpa's Barn - Patricia D. Richards, 1992

grandpa's barn

Remembering those things that have crossed the cosmos of one's memory is oft times a daunting if not impossible task. Through time, the adventures we have known become tiny atoms of our lives, tenuous and delicate beyond belief. Left neglected, these scintillas of time fade and spin away from us toward some far-flung galaxy light years beyond recall, where they languish for some time, then spin away again toward the darkest corners of the universe—to a place where all that was joyous and wonderful, all that we were and had become will be hidden beyond the reaches of our minds. Eternally forgotten.

Don't let this happen.

Clench the slender ribbons of the past and pull it closer, ever closer, until yesterday's songs and laughter shine bright and clear as your tomorrows. Once they are caught and tethered to your heart and mind, you will be stunned by the striking beauty and eminent grace of the past that belonged once to you.

Tell me, have I ridden so far afield that I have lost my way? Has the rutted path of years doubled back upon time itself, leading me again to this remembered place? And how have the willows grown so tall since I stood here as a child?

It seems but moments ago that I slipped from the saddle to explore Grandpa's barn. Surely, the lathered sweat, like soapsuds, is still beading from Jerry's withers. He stands now, hitched to the pole fence, and in repose casts an umber shadow on the yellow heat of this pastured afternoon.

From every aspect, Grandpa Charlie's barn appears to have sprouted from the land. It stands with shoulders squared against the earth and sky, bigger than the imagination. The aged pathway to its entrance bears a necklace of river rock and beckons one to a weathered Dutch door that is, in truth, an artifact. Doug-fir built, square-nailed, and cross-braced, it shows the marks of a drawknife and hand plane, tools of a different era and different men.

I push with both hands; and finally, dragging its feet in reluctance, the door creaks open on cinnamon-colored hinges. They were fashioned on a forge long ago made cold by passing years, and their rusted hinge pins shriek and set to flight a jay sunning in the grass fifty yards away.

As I step over the crumbling threshold, my thoughtless intrusion terrorizes some tiny unseen creature; and now, together, we share this barn—his eminent domain—a silent, half-lit cathedral of sensual wonders, which only in age I can now articulate.

From high on the weathered siding where freezing winter winds have scored a terrible toll, cracks and splits in the ancient planks cast a yellow geometry of sunlight on the dusted earth that has floored this place for more than a century. It is a warming light, a burnishing and softening of everything inside, and it matches completely the pervasive quiet and abiding memories I find here.

From the coarse board walls hang every type of implement imaginable: a catacomb of old hay rakes, bits of horse tack looped over wooden pegs, a cast-iron wheel, and rusted shovel. Here, an ancient anvil spiked to a tree stump, and beside it, a grinding wheel. A rusted branding iron is impaled on a spike, and a wagon singletree lies awkwardly askew in a nest of broken wagon wheels whose miles are far behind them. A high cantle saddle, dusted with the patina of time, sits astride the rail of a horse stall, and a hayfork rests tiredly against the creaking stairs leading to the loft above.

An ebbing memory strives to recall it all, but there is simply too much here to be remembered. The sight of the tools and tack of another era have been

Barn Door - Edward C. Larson, 2017

The Wheelwright Shop, Montana - from the Author's Collection

From every aspect, Grandpa Charlie's barn
appears to have sprouted from the land.
It stands with shoulders squared against the earth and sky,

Grandpa's Barn II - Patricia D. Richards, 2000

bigger than.
imagination.

swallowed up by the years that have rushed by since I was a child on horseback and first entered this enchanted place.

But the smell of this darkened sanctuary is a living thing—part horse, part leather, part earth, part sky. It is rich beyond belief and brings to mind the essence of all things real and intangible that constitute the value of this land and its people. Were it a song, the melody would be the faint odor of hay, sage, and cottonwood; the arpeggio: the sweat and shit of horses; then the counterpoint: rusted iron, worn and weathered traces and reins, old liniments and axle grease, pack rats and swallows, and a million nuances of other scents from things living and dead. This dwelling must be savored and sipped like good wine. Seasoned by the salt and pepper of gone-by years, the dark air here cooks and bubbles in the warmth of this sunshiny afternoon. It will remain with me in quiet hours of remembrance perhaps longer and sweeter than anything else I've experienced.

I leave the rich shadows of the barn, blinking against the brilliance of the sun, never suspecting with a child's mind that the memories of just being in this place will last a lifetime. I walk thirty yards to the edge of the Stillwater River running cold and clear on its eternal pathway between the willows and the quaking aspen. It speaks the same language as other rivers of its kind, but with a dialogue that seems gentler, more personal, and more compelling because of my identification with this place and the people whose lives are set here. Lying on the green volunteer grass of the riverbank, I push my face down into the flashing ripples and drink in its aching coldness. It is better than the homemade ginger ale Grandpa Charlie aged under the kitchen sink.

With the imagination of the very young, it is easy for me to picture a small group of Crow braves pausing to rest at this very spot. Their bareback ponies are muzzled deep in the river's vibrant shallows while the riders converse in Apsáalooke on the disappointing results of the hunt. They have ridden the high ridges since daylight, their horses are tired, and they have found nothing in this day but searing yellow heat and this blessed cool water. And perhaps that is enough.

My child's reverie is broken when Walter and Ralph, Grandpa's nephews, shout from the veranda for me to put Jerry back in the pole corral. Each day in the early morning, these brothers have saddled him for me and turned my stay here into a lifetime adventure. This ranch has become a part of me…a good horse, a black saddle, and the tall yellowed grass of the plains, which I have seen before only in a picture show in the city where I live. They have taught me of hay rakes and wagons, of water pumps and rifles, and of the warmth of kerosene lamps whose wicks burn with the light of long ago.

The horse and saddle put away, I turn once more to this barn that Grandpa created with scarred hands and a body made strong by need. Shadowed now, and with the patience of the very old, it waits in dignity as the sun steps down beyond the timberline to start its journey toward another day.

Even as a child, I knew this barn would not be here forever. Someday, it will be gone, shredded by the savage winds and terrible cold that assault this place and its people as a simple matter of course.

But for now, I can embrace it—not as a place—but rather as a wondrous experience.

I push the rebellious stall door closed in deference to the small creature I terrorized with my entrance. He can remain safe and secure within our sanctuary. I will not pass this way again for seventy-six years.

Saint Giles Church - Edward C. Larson, 1984

forever

Don't reckon my years by the hours of their days.

If you would tally up my time,
    count me by the loves that I have known,
    both young and old,
    and by the hearts
    and hopes
    I have held in the hollows of my hands.

Count me by the dreams
    that passing years have washed away
    leaving me poorer,
    and yet, richer.

What you see in me, I am.
What you feel in me, I have been and known.

My days have been hard and loved,
    made of minutes and hours sheaved
    like tall brown grass,
    wrapped by sensual pleasure,
    tears,
    and laughter.

Rain and snow have played
    across the clock face of my years—
    measuring the passing moment more precisely
    than a clicking wheel.

Bright hours and darkness
    have set for me the cadence of my mind,
    directing me constantly
    toward pathways I have never walked before.

Don't make a pendulum of me.
I am a thing past clocks and time.
I am a life that has loved.

I.
  am.
    forever.

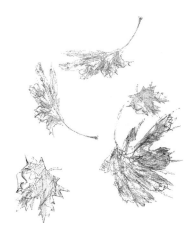

trilogy

The aged wind, which seems the mantra of this tenuous oasis, rustles the red leaves of my memory…blowing them back across the prairie grass and the dry, brittle years of yesterday.

In the throaty voices of times gone by, it whispers to me that these children who languish in the shaded sunlight of July are, in truth, a parody of what once I knew and now labor to remember. They are mirror images of Jeff and Eddie and the town girl running in joy across the fields of a 1934 Montana afternoon.

The Fishtail General Store - Patricia D. Richards, 1992

They are **mirror images**
of Jeff and Eddie
and the town girl

running in joy across the fields of a 1934 Montana afternoon.

We were older, but by little, and the meadows of this Crow land, sweet with the knee-high stalks of summer, were wonderlands to be explored and conquered.

For short weeks, I lived the life my grandfather had lived and loved. There was a good saddle horse named Jerry and a rolling block .22 to shoot jackrabbits and tin cans set atop rotting fence posts.

We three swam in the Rosebud and fished the Stillwater, awaiting the new adventure of each day with a common joy, then slept on straw-ticked pads in a ranch house lit only with the wraith-like flame of a kerosene lamp as old as time.

I left this storied place in sadness to return to the autumn rains that wetted the pitiful Depression dwellings of my town, carrying in the saddle bag of my mind the dreams that summer left with me.

Weeks after my return, Gram took me aside to tell me of the letter from her sister….Jeff had died of burns drying his clothes after a swim in the Rosebud.

It was my first brush with death, and I hated its color on the palette of my life.

And of the town girl, willow-like and haunting?

I see her in the quiet times I give to reverie. Her eyes seem filled with all the good and bad of the years between us, and I am deeply troubled by the fact that I cannot recall her name.

Simple Promise - Edward C. Larson, 2005

a simple promise

love
I speak of it with certain hesitation—
for how can one describe the warmth
that fills the rain-laced fields of winter
with all the promise
of an early and eternal spring?

untaught
and still so exquisitely learned,
it fills the tenderness of age—
and makes the older heart expand.

seen
through the eyes,

felt
through the hands and heart,
it strolls in grace and elegance
the pages of our years
and in the end,
grants that which all the world must seek:

the simple promise
that we shall not be forgotten.

collecting

It is given to every man
to know
the morning
with its transient allotment
of diamond-studded fields
and flowers.

He can know summer noon,
when the earth
and all its creatures
simmer gently
on God's front burner.

And above all,
he may know
eventide,
when his world is filled
with that special tranquility,
peace,
and
love
that makes the universe
worthwhile.

Birds, hills, love, and flowers are free.

Should a man fail
to collect
his allotted share,
he will stand on the edge of forever
with his pockets empty,
and his dreams
unfilled.

Big Sky Riders - Edward C. Larson, 2000

the gospel
according to matthew

For generations, my cousins have been herdsmen, tillers, and scions of their pastoral lands. In the process, they have become so intertwined with their earth and their herds that man, land, and beast have joined in an age-old and inseparable trilogy. Here are the sheep of a Montana meadow deep in August...they are the sheep of cousins, Louis, Amelia, and Matthew. The flock rests beside the river in a sylvan setting that is, quite simply, stunning in its primal beauty and peace...and eternal in its reality.

We stand quietly *admidst*

Along the Stillwater - Patricia D. Richards, 1992

the serenity of the sheep
and the lengthening shadows...

But in a broader sense, there is an immensity here that transcends the idyllic perfection of this time and place, a symbolism that leaves one breathless with its implications. The culture of shepherd and flock has remained a constant for more than ten thousand years, a stewardship stretching unbroken in time from the Kazakh steppes of Central Asia to the banks of the Stillwater on this fading afternoon.

For those somehow chosen through sheer circumstance or the vagaries of fate, the role of shepherd most surely begins with the inborn imperative to deliver, protect, and sustain the flock placed in his or her care. That relationship, a seeming mandate from birth, crosses continents, cultures, and time itself and becomes the common denominator tethering this day and my cousins to the ages.

We stand quietly amidst the serenity of the sheep and the lengthening shadows of the cottonwood and aspen lining the banks of this small, wondrous river. It is the shank of the day. We four "city mice" cluster about Matthew and listen intently to a litany of happenings from the book of his life. His voice gently turns each page, extolling the intricacies of a lifestyle eons removed from our own. It is a book we have never before bothered to read.

The volume is couched in the value structures and responsibilities of his thirty-three years on this range. Passages speak of the oppressive heat of summer and shocking cold of winter. He speaks of the threat of predation and range fires, the birthing of new generations, the tilling, the harvesting, the desperate wanting of rain, and the despair of a crop or herd gone bad.

There is an utter fascination between the covers of Matthew's words. A meld of herdsman-slash-classical-pianist, there is as much of the Masai Mara within him as there is the provenance of Handel or Bach.

I draw away from the group and walk toward the river to assimilate the things I have heard. The sands of the afternoon have nearly run out of the glass, and the Stillwater has darkened to an exquisite shade of amber. Here and there, in hues I cannot describe, are dark holes of still water. They swirl below the staccato of the riffles, shielding the Rainbows and Brownies sequestered there. I would think the rise might begin within an hour or so…it would be a time for Royal Coachmen or Wooly Buggers, or perhaps a Black Gnat carefully laid down crosscurrent. I know now in an instant that Grandpa and I would be sharing together the timeless soul of this river, save for more than a century that has elbowed its way between us.

Turning back from the river, I see Matthew and my three cousins framed against the background of the undulating prairie. The hills rise to the west and top-out in the cobalt of the slowly darkening sky.

There is still enough sun to brush the hills with brilliant yellow—and enough shade to turn the shadows of the cottonwood and aspen to the richest emerald I have ever known.

The scene is classic Vincent van Gogh, an unheralded Montana grain field filled with all the movement, drama, and texture of his painting, *A Wheatfield with Crows*.

It is painted now only by the sinking prairie sun, in a land the tortured genius of Arles never knew.

Old Post Office, Wales - Edward C. Larson, 2005

once loved

To be once loved is surely quite enough—
for that certainty,
the pages of our years
can be turned back
with smiles and tenderness
to those fine hours and days
when the heart knew laughter,
and time was filled
with all the sunshine
of belonging.

And though the years of being quite alone
may intervene,
and winds and snows of winter
may for some short time
darken the corners of the heart,
to be once loved
is surely
quite
enough.

Dead Owl - Edward C. Larson, 1999

dead owl

At first, it was only a joke
between Whitey and Monty and me,
but they brought her in, broke-winged and dead.
Must have been huntin' the Jackson road at night
and ran into a goddamn Kenworth windshield.
'Least that's what it looked like;
and I remember sayin',
"Everyone ought to have a stuffed owl."

Now she's clutched in a piss-fir branch
and roosts on the end of my roll-top,
staring through brown glass eyes
that will never see a mouse or the moon.

The wing backs are reddish,
    like leaves of autumn a long time under the tree;
    and the talons are curled and sharper than hell,
    like a Chinese actor's fingernails.

The feel of her belly and breast
    is the way I sense her now;
    the feathers are soft as night wood smoke
    I stroke with the back of my hand.

I feel life in the body that used to be
    and wish she could fly away
    to have one more night in a live oak patch,
    down close where the river runs.

The hunt would begin in a purple world;
    the sun passed on for an hour or more.
    The wind would slip through her feathers,
    silent as anything,
    while her fire eyes swept the riverbank
    seeking the rustling sound,
    and afterward, spitting it up in a ball
    no bigger than a baby's fist.

The touch, I guess, is the thing.
    A barn owl's belly feels good.

Too bad she lived in a time and place
    where there's so damn many windshields
    and so few owls.

II

Delicious autumn!
My very soul is wedded to it...
- George Eliot -

the harbor

If Thoreau had Walden Pond, I have the Harbor—I mean it's that important to me...a thread of life, a part of my time, an animated segment of my being, my special place! On daily walks, I can submerge myself in the adventure of it...in the sights, sounds, and smells of it; and for the next few paragraphs, I wish you'd join me while I share what's in my head.

There's a light southwesterly blowing this afternoon. I stand on the east jetty looking out toward the sea. The sun picks up the lace of waves breaking out across the entrance: blue, white, green, blue-white-green…a panorama of colors as old as the earth, an eternal kaleidoscope turning exclusively for me. Beyond the jetties, out where the bay picks up that cerulean blue, I can hear the mile buoy clearing its throat. Today, through the mist of four hundred years, I can imagine Sebastian Vizcaino, square-rigged and cautious, threading his way slowly beyond Lighthouse Point, looking around, then heading back to Acapulco and telling the viceroy of New Spain that Monterey Bay is "sheltered from the winds." A so-so navigator but a damn liar!

With some reluctance, I turn from the sea and walk northward past the "Laurel and Hardy comedy" of Sunday afternoons on the launch ramp where Budweiser, booze, and brine make weekend boaters sink their pickups. Beside me, the patina on the granite boulders turns to a green-brown sheen, painted by billions of intertidal things that are walking about this afternoon, just like me. It's an arena for herons, which mix hope with faith and come up with enough anchovies to survive and honk at those who invade their space.

I always stop at the fishermen's dock and mostly think about my dad who taught me how to tie hooks and pull nets. He also taught me to revel in the smell of creosote, diesel oil, old fish, and old boats…and how to love the sea.

There are men here who are a part of my life, *thank God*! These are guys to be studied, anachronisms from another time and space who spend a lifetime on the sea and end up owing for it. And like my friend Victor, when their faces turn to leather, their arms don't work, and their fingers are arthritic and curved like owl's talons, they cling to their boats and their freedom and know that their lives have been treasures to live.

And now I am once more walking toward the open sea.

The west jetty stretches out into the deeper water — a bastion of boulders and tetrapods, wrapping its protective arm about everything inside and smelling of the foam of fractured waves. From the beginning, I have walked through a wonder place of renewal, of dynamic life and moving beauty where nothing is still, and nothing is static—birds, sea, sun, and sky changing, changing with a richness that is never ever the same.

I trust telling you about this is one way to express a profound and grateful thanks.

Anchored - Edward C. Larson, 2000

sole ownership

Before my sweeping eyes, I can now see
no other soul,
and all these things belong to me:
a freshing wind,
a seabird's cry,
the fresh-washed sand...
and I, the one and only owner of this day
that's painted quite completely shades of gray.

Perhaps it's foolish for one person to demand
sole ownership, at any time,
of earth or sea or land.

I could be coaxed to share it
if I could but find
another standing near
with just my turn of mind.

But sharing this day's time can never be,
for as I've said before,
though all about I've searched,
there's not another soul for me to see.

Perhaps it's just as well;
I need not share this stormy day
nor let some other drink from this,
my cup of endless gray.

For it's a sure and certain thing,
a day as gray as this turned out to be
may well be loved by me.
But in this whole wide world about
may not be yet another's cup of tea.

Harbor - Edward C. Larson, 2005

walton light—
santa cruz harbor

Like an errant phoenix, she rises from the craggy geneses of her beginnings. Then with defiant dignity, her timeworn fingers strip bare the banality of this day's passing times and tides, casting each aside to be lost forever on the morrow's wind.

The simple drama of her constant presence impales, with wondrous clarity, the morning's scourge of fog or that stygian blackness that is the face of night upon the sea.

Walton Lighthouse - Edward C. Larson, 2005

Her light, a simple lantern filled with solace and salvation, breathes in concert with her spoken words, each becoming a single latchkey to the booming welcome of her open door.

Hear her voice of patent longing, at once a metaphoric hymn of joy sung by all of heaven's angels. Thence again, her mournful lamentations for those who've fallen through the outstretched hands of circumstance to know, with infinite reality, the perils of once and future seas.

The sun and I have grown old watching the shadows of your being sweep across the sands of time we've shared. Through the golden glory of the morning, we feel the warmth and texture of your reaching arms and hear the many psalms you've sung to us. With us forever shall remain your thrilling trilogy:

   ≋ the limitless magic of your deepest seas;

   ℃ the green meadows, which carpet the highlands of the earth;

   ☾ the star-laden universe, twirling a cable's length above the shining light of your weathered tower.

Within the grace and comfort of your ceaseless vigil, we see and know these things.

Abide with me.

Three Irish Lords - Edward C. Larson, 2000

fish dock

As dawn grows older and the day comes on, the air fills with sea sounds and the smell of where fish were. A black dog named Misery lifts his leg against a dumpster. Four-letter words and diesel smoke hang suspended in the morning, the legacy of fishermen who belong to this place. These are men who will not sell stocks or wear neckties because there is too much "boy" left in them. Long ago, a daily fix of fun and adventure robbed them of reason and destroyed their capability to determine whether they live to fish or fish to live. It is that dichotomy that dooms them to sail endlessly across a sea of empty wallets and unpaid mooring bills and to find in that journey an exquisite peace and harmony.

But few leave this pursuit. Like roulette players, they are sustained by the certainty that tomorrow will be better. Each day, the players in this game are annealed into a lifestyle of nonpolluted solitude and hope, in an equilibrium of sea, sky, and being. Each night, with their red and green running lights sharpened by darkness, they return to the tranquility and silence of the harbor and await the adventure of tomorrow. In retrospect, winning or losing seems rather unimportant when compared with the joy of belonging.

Change is a part of the magic of the harbor's fascination. The vagaries of wind and rain, clouds, and sun modify and shape the images that have become such a feast for me. Each is a being with a voice and a message for the listener. The southerly wind speaks with a loud roar. It hammers its fist against the bastion of the west jetty, promising hell to pay if it lasts long enough. The easterly is often a pleasant breath. If I work the jib and main just right, its gentleness can carry my pretty gaff-rigged Monterey soft and steady from the mile buoy right into our slip at G-39. That rarely happens; but when it does, it's a sailing triumph — *try that with a Santa Cruz 27!* I built my boat for that; nobody else can do it.

The heart of this harbor is the heartbeat of its people…good and bad. I have my idols here.

Mr. Hendricks, a kind and gentle soul, crushes aluminum cans and wheels them in his grocery cart up to the recycler—one trip a day—always smiling, a man of worth. Ah...there's my dear friend Victor Ghio, of whom I've already spoken—the personification of the Genovese fisherman. He is an icon of the harbor and the sea. He is terribly small, but he's a man with the heart of a lion. His boat, the *Catherina G.*, is a product of his own hands—built fifty years ago at Pasquinucci's Boat Building Works in Sausalito. In the worst of weather, they need no compass to find the harbor entrance—only intuition. The man and his boat and his brother John are totally important to me, and all are too precious to lose.

And I can tell you about Paul Groszman, fisherman and skipper of the *Tuna*, who performed his own personal miracle on a black night in October 1953; and Sam Mazzarino, whose life was a chronicle of triumph and tragedy that reads like a Hemingway novel—I can tell you about him, too.

There is a story in each of the people I see each day, whose lives, hopes, disappointments, and dreams are as much a part of the harbor as the gulls and channel markers. I can speak to you of tides and pinnipeds, of sailing physics and kelp, or of the canyon, lingcod, Monterrey clippers, western grebe, or Heermann's gulls. I can show you the nesting spots of the blue herons, and I know the paths of Arana Gulch and who the hell John Woods was and why you don't cleat down the main sheet in heavy weather. I can tick off

The *heart* of this harbor...

The Boat Store - Edward C. Larson, 1997

the *heartbeat* of its people...

the names of a jillion harbor people who have freely given to me the priceless gift of their friendship: Mustafa, Mary Jane, Kimbra and Kinnamon, Brian Foss and Barbara, Gorge and Arturo, and Mr. Hendricks. I have changed dramatically in the near-twenty years since I came here. These people and this place have been the engine of that change.

One could look a lifetime to discover what I have found within the confines of the harbor and within the worth of its people. Essentially, it's the intense feeling of belonging to a place and to those who share a measure of its value. I have had the rare privilege of sharing their interests and their fortunes, good or bad. The Sandy Tuckers, Charlie Taylors, Joe Bendricks, and others I know here are important in my life, and I wouldn't trade them for anything I've known to date…and *God knows*, I've been around long enough to know whereof I speak.

Phil's Fish Market - Edward C. Larson, 2000

harbor invitation

Early on this morning, I sensed a change.
Passing close abeam the west jetty
in the half-light of this dawning,
there was a restlessness,
a change in breathing of the Southwest swell.
It'll be well to moor the boat quickly and take my walk
if one is to be taken this day.

Though I have walked this way a thousand times,
the adventure is as new and changing as tomorrow.

High in the eucalyptus trees across the way,
the just-born heron cries from a used nest.
And my friend Rob,
whose shoulders and spirit are immense
but who cannot walk at all,
forgot his kayak paddle.
Left it on the dock.
I'll pick it up.
That kayak is his magic carpet,
a way out of aluminum crutches
that I wish he didn't have to use.

The wind is shifting northerly;
there is a gray above the heritage oak in Arana Gulch.
I smell rain.

From the west jetty, hull down,
I think I see Victor Ghio's *Catherina G.*
He'll be in the gaff hatch catching salmon
with hands that ache from seventy years
of rock cod and thresher shark.

There's magic here
in hulls and masts and spars;
but the fabric of faces and lives
interwoven with an ancient sea
is the treasure of this refuge, I've found.

I'll share it with you, any day,
when water mountains break white in violence
across the entrance,
or in evening solitude
when quiet wings are all that you can hear.

So, an invitation:
take off your shoes—
I'd like it if you'd leave bare footprints here,
beside mine,
in a place
that belongs
to each of us.

requiem

I'm sure there's one common bond we share; or in all likelihood, you'd not be here today. But your interest or preoccupation with boats and our harbor is probably not compulsive/obsessive—not as strong as mine. For nearly eighteen years, I have roamed the harbor until it has become, quite simply, a thing of living value to me. A thing to be unwrapped each day, examined, polished, and cherished, then rewrapped in a tissue of the day's memories and returned to its drawer in my mind. Its ever-changing face, voice, and activity have, thankfully, become something I cannot do without.

In finding it, I have, in turn, more easily found myself; and for that, I am eternally grateful.

There is sadness in the harbor, too. Commercial fishing is in great trouble. Too many people have taken too many fish for too long. My friend Victor Ghio and others like him catch fish with a hook and line. They have been victimized by huge factory trawlers, driftnets, and ineffective governmental regulations. Their livelihood is dying. Several years ago, I wrote this piece after talking with Victor. His words are the eulogy for an ancient art form and a preamble for the end of a lifestyle.

> I heard 'em say there's nothing out there,
> at least down to sixty fathoms;
> and you know damn well,
> dreams are gonna rust
> like cheap trolling wire.

> Oh, maybe a few shakers and a jumper now and then,
> but the swells mask a scary emptiness.
> You could go to sleep in the gaff hatch,
> and a day's catch ain't enough
> to pay for diesel and a six-pack.

> The docks look like a goddamn porcupine—
> masts and poles weaving around,
> halyards bangin'—
> ain't no boats out;
> they're all here.

My friend Victor Ghio and others like him catch fish
with a hook and line.

Victor Ghio and Catherina G. - Edward C. Larson, 2000

Commercial fishing is in great trouble.

They float in the green harbor swill,
like wallflowers at the dance,
or hookers on chintz cushions
waiting to turn a trick.

Want to see diesel smoke?
Just somebody start a whisper
that there's bait balls
showing out beyond the buoy.

But I got it on good authority—
Victor told me over a short Miller's—
there ain't nothin' out there
this side of the sixty-fathom line.

The sky's quiet, but the wind wanders
looking for a place to cause trouble.
Dock drizzle covers everything
and makes the morning wet and cold to touch.
It's a time for boats to worry.

The dumpsters are too full of last week
for the tops to close.
They sit with open mouths
full of seine twine,
rotten apitong,
rusted sheaves,
dead zincs,
and dreams that weren't well-hooked
and got away.

You can smell "discourage" in the morning:
guys needing a shave
and something to believe in;
but like Victor told me,
there's nothin' out there,
at least this side of the sixty-fathom line.

They congregate and cuss,
drink beer, and smoke Camels;
but I've seen 'em looking toward the bay,
seeking an answer,
somewhere out there,
from an empty sea
they can't understand.

Decks are painted,
engines bright and tight and running,
the boats waltz gently in the morning.
It's really only for the music to begin....

But sumthin's wrong, God knows,
and I think He's talked to Victor
because Victor, he told me early on over a short Miller's,
there really ain't nothin' out there
this side of the sixty-fathom line.

I see in my boat and our harbor more a state of mind
than a possession and a place. I have found dynamism
here, a collation of weather, seas, people, and times that
assail my thinking and all my senses with a daily
changing fare—always exciting, always romantic,

always satisfying and story filled. I find priceless solitude in a fog-filled morning of early August when the sounds and edges of the world are wrapped in that quiet silence birthed by the mists. The foghorn, for me never intrusive, carries with it, at once, the essence of the water world of which it is so much a part.

Oft times on such mornings, I've experienced the blending of the foghorn and the low moan of the whistle on the one-mile buoy…and there is nothing like that duet that can speak so profoundly of the sea.

marilyn

I long to fly to that thin line
that separates the sky and the sea.

Won't you go with me?

To that far place where gulls at night
must surely wend their way;
and then, at break of day,
return to circle, glide, and dive
above the endless surf and sand....

Please. Take my hand—
and go with me.

Together, we might cross the thin and tender line
that proves the birth of day
and cradle of the night....

I wish you might...
go with me.

I know I've always played the fool;
in fact, I've made it quite my special rule
to follow each gull's song.
I've yearned with all my heart (in full futility)
to fly along.

I cannot make the trip alone,
across the gray and empty sea.

And if this dream of mine can ever be,
you must *go with me.*

a remembered realm
of wind and weather

"I spent many magnificent days aboard the Doris E. She was one of the cannery tenders owned by my dad's cannery, and she became my window on Alaska. I literally grew up working her decks while listening to the heartbeat of her huge diesel engine."

— Edward C. Larson, *Spear-Carrier in a Backwater War*

The realm in which the Doris E. played out her life and times lies in that portion of southeast Alaska located in the immediate vicinity of the Alexander Archipelago. Sometimes called the ABC Islands, Admiralty, Baranof, and

Chichagof are the dominant northern islands in the group. This trilogy of timbered beauty stands aloof in the harsh gray waters off the Alaskan coastline, mimicking the shapes of huge stone arrow points chipped from the continent by some stupendous tectonic upheaval in eons far beyond memory.

I have traveled the world; and yet, to me, these islands represent the ultimate in romance, primal culture, and sheer exquisite beauty to be found on our planet. Those who walk the margins of these fabled islands stand in the company of a treasure trove of terrestrial, bird, and marine wildlife seen nowhere else. The apex predator of these islands, the great Alaskan brown bear, roams the beaches, meadows, and highlands in large numbers, begging the visiting interloper to walk hand in hand with caution, respect, and a small dollop of fear.

The whole of the archipelago is surrounded by a maze of treacherously complex channels and passages filled with bizarre wave patterns and currents, constituting a never-ending challenge and threat to those navigating these inland waters.

My ancient chart, poorly folded and "graffitied" by old loran coordinates and course lines, sets forth an intriguing litany of warnings about the violence of this place while totally ignoring its inherent majesty. It is quite simply a land so incredibly unique that it must be experienced to be believed. From the storm-ridden Gulf of Alaska to the west, a broad corridor of water dotted with islands runs eastward past the northern end of Chichagof Island. The passage known as Icy Strait opens on the northern end into the incomparable magnificence of Glacier Bay. It then turns southeastward and is blunted by the Mansfield Peninsula and the western shores of Admiralty Island where it is split into two separate segments or straits. The body of water heading north becomes Lynn Canal. The channel leading southward is called Chatham Strait. The latter forms a wide passage separating Admiralty Island from its sister to the west.

These straits are huge, rough "sea rivers," and each has its own unique capability to maul or destroy the careless or uninitiated. Lynn Canal has been described as a funnel of horrible winds and storms and was the scene of one of the great tragedies in Alaska maritime history.

On an October day in 1918, the Canadian steamer *Princess Sophia* ran aground on Vanderbilt Reef. Although appearing to be in no immediate danger, she issued a distress call to which many vessels in the vicinity responded. Because of heavy sea and winds, the captain of the *Princess Sophia* refused to remove the passengers and crew and decided instead to spend the night secure on the reef until the next morning's favorable tide and weather. During the night, the winds increased, and a heavy snowfall covered the sea. Sometime after midnight, the *Princess Sophia* slid off the reef and sank like a stone carrying three hundred and forty-three passengers and crew to their deaths.

A dog found the next day was the lone survivor.

The whole of this water empire seethes with monumental natural forces, constantly effective movement, and changes in its venue. It is a place of mountains whose glaciers shed themselves into its wild and wind-torn straits. The straits, in turn, are lined with a thousand reefs and torturous passages demanding constant vigilance and respect. Tides of mammoth proportion create rushing currents with speeds often greater than of the small indigenous vessels that work and die here. Historic winds and breath-stopping rains constitute the normal weather pattern; while below the surface, the constant shifting of continental plates makes the magnetic compass shudder with confusion and disbelief. Tidal waves paired with the ongoing threat of massive earthquakes: it is not an easy place for the sedentary soul.

The elemental face of this land and its seas has changed dramatically in the geological wink of an eye that has passed since I was a child. Since the 1920s and '30s, glaciers have receded, and extensive shoaling has occurred. Following the great earthquakes of 1958 and 1964, massive magnetic reorientation has confounded marine navigation. The entire area remains in a state of flux, a place filled with vibrant élan and endless beauty. It is a single living entity bathed in the constancy of change in which nothing is static or benign.

The birth of another season on a cannery tender begins in the spring a thousand miles to the south in

Seattle's "hiring halls." Alaska, with its wind and weather, is only a deck hand's last-year remembrance. Through the wintertime, some have lived in comfortable homes with dedicated families. Those less fortunate have frequented the skid roads of South Seattle, grasping at straws to stay alive until the beginning of the new salmon season. Old hands, known entities who have served on the tenders in prior years, are hired first; new, wannabe hires must wait their turn in the hope of placement. Crewmen who have served on tenders for years are often hired several months in advance to paint, repair, and refurbish the boats before their spring trek to the north.

Finally, the boarding lines that have bound the tenders to their berths in Lake Union are cast free, and the eight-hundred-mile pilgrimage to Alaska and the salmon grounds begins. Should the tender be assigned the arduous task of heavy tow, the journey will be made at the maddening pace of three to four knots at best, making the vessel a tethered goat in the realm of roaming-tiger storms. If a vessel is unburdened, a prudent captain can speedily seek shelter from a storm; if the vessel is burdened with a heavy tow, escape is not always possible. In my time aboard the *Doris E.*, dependable weather forecasting was eons away; and more often than not, violence struck without warning. In early spring and late fall, oft-voiced fears of bad weather hung over the boats and their crews like a sword tied to the overhead with a length of darning thread.

On the journey to and from Alaska, two bodies of water open to the wickedness of the west. The first to be encountered, Queen Charlotte Sound, exposes a transiting vessel to the possibility of assault for a distance of about thirty-eight miles. Crossing for an elegant cruise ship or a thirty-foot troller can often be worse than expected. Each year, the *Doris E.* and her crew tiptoed north and south through the sound's vagaries, oft times finding it as peaceful as a millpond — at other times, filled with hardship and trouble as Queen Charlotte displayed all the terrible rage of a woman scorned. Surely it is safe to say that once the crossing was made, visible relief was etched on the face of every crew member on board, particularly Fred Foster, the elderly cook whose galley had been laid awry and awash more than once by a three-thousand-mile punch that began in the South Bering Sea.

The second window open to the west is Dixon Entrance, a volatile domain of wind, tide, and weather, and a place I have considered as evil since I was a child. In years to come, I would fight my own demons crossing these waters. This vicious, testing sea lies just south of Dall and Prince of Wales Islands, whose two southern capes, Cape Muzon to the west and Cape Chacon to the east are dreaded by mariners and spoken of in soft tones before quiet December firesides. It's a place I have symbolized as the land of the black puking cormorant — a bird I detest. Flying arrow straight across wind-topped waves, these vile birds seem an agent whose very presence speaks of threatening evil and death.

The dreaded drama of Dixon Entrance occurs when the villainous trilogy of wind, tides, and weather conspire to destroy the unthinking or unwary, and this assault can be unexpected and final.

From open passage to the west, all the Gulf of Alaska's violence is free to rush toward the shoreline, manifesting itself into monstrous swells and confusing seas; while from the north, Cordova Bay and Tlevak Strait empty their immense containment of water twice daily, sending the flow south to collide with the tempest of current and swell moving east from the open Pacific. From these dual sources, the cauldrons collide between Cape Muzon and Cape Chacon in a maelstrom of monumental proportions. Rushing wind from the northwest or southwest can then collaborate to carve the waters into immense and vicious storms that challenge description. In a shockingly short period of time, Dixon Entrance can become an unbridled horror.

Late in the fishing season of 1938, Frederick Bushman, just twenty-one and a member of my extended family, served as a crew member on the purse seiner *Eidsvold*, working out of the cannery at Waterfall on the south end of Prince of Wales Island. She went down unseen and without a sound, leaving only her broken skiff and a torn life preserver on the rocky and hostile shoreline just north of Cape Muzon. For months following the tragedy, Fred's brother Richard, my schoolmate and closest friend, was tortured by dreams that Fred was stranded on the beach on the western shore of Dall Island, shivering in the bitter cold and wind and crying out to their mother and father for rescue. For more than sixty years, the specter of Frederick's death and Richard's nightmares has painted my thoughts about this lonely and forbidding place where Fred died.

As a young boy, I was blessed to be befriended by Philip Hastin. Phil was a true waterman. Born on the shores of Puget Sound, he found a beloved future as a crewman and captain of fishing vessels in Southeast Alaska. As a teenager, I was privileged to work for and learn about boats and the sea from this man who loved them both. The following account was related to me by Phil when he was serving as first mate on the *Doris E.* Always tempering fear with understanding and eloquent preparation, he was a master mariner who also shared my deep feelings regarding the treachery of Dixon Entrance and its frightful harbinger, the black cormorant.

By all accounts, 1937 had been a decent year. Mid-April saw the *Doris E.* in the company of Dall's porpoises moving north in quiet weather, creasing the glistening waters of the Strait of Georgia with a bow wave of confidence and expectation. As usual, there were orca pods blowing in Johnstone Strait; and greige granite shores and verdant forests rolled by, virginal, glorious, and unbroken, save for the sight of an occasional small anchored troller sunning herself in an inlet. Wispy strands of high cirrus clouds with their ends turned up crisscrossed the sky, and breeze from the *Doris E.*'s own passage was the sole wind aboard.

The morning silence was broken only by the sound of Fred Foster's pots and pans and Kato's humming. The crew no longer heard the constant rumble of the diesel or recognized it as a part of their stream of consciousness. Owen Hagan held to the eastern shore of Hecate Strait; and by the time they were abeam Cape George, the *Doris E.* had been snugged down for the fifty-mile crossing of Dixon Entrance. Now, a slight westerly, like a flickering flame, had birthed itself somewhere far out at sea, but its placidness spoke more of tranquility than violence.

Fred Foster had washed the morning dishes and spread a dampened cloth on the galley table. The catsup and malt vinegar bottles and "canned cow" container had been laid flat or braced to meet any threat ahead. Sandwich makings and four cans of brisling sardines were spread out across the wet tablecloth, sure to survive any rolling or pitching. Some midmorning coffee cups were washed, dried, and placed in the bottom of the galley sink, new coffee was brewed, and the iron bars were tightly set—staggered across the top of the cookstove to keep pots in place.

Foster tottered aft to his stateroom and moved his beloved Underwood typewriter from its place on the small desk to safety on the cabin floor by his bunk. Up since four o'clock, he would rest for a while for whatever lay ahead.

Galley Kitchen ~ Edward C. Larson, 2000
Letter and Photo of Ed Larson, Captain Phil Hastin, and Harold "Jorgy" Jorgensen
from the Author's Collection

Dear Dad,

It's been a hell of a trip. We were doing fine comin' up Johnstone Strait till we got abeam of Port Hardy. wind picked up real bad, and we got a mix of snow zing rain. The tail shaft bearing was heating up had to slow her down. By that time, the waves and so bad she was rollin' her rails under, and I had ght lose her abeam of Pine Island. I had un sick they were sloshin' back and forth in

By now, Phil Hastin had double lashed the skiff aft of the galley stack, checked the latches on the lazaret, then tied the massive manila fenders tightly against the toe rail. They tended to swing outboard in a heavy sea. He slowly made his way about the deck checking the closure of cabin doors and windows, latching and pinning the fo'c's'le head doors, and looking aloft to the topping lift and to its proper belay at the port pin rail. All seemed secure. With final satisfaction, he climbed back up to the wheelhouse, lit another Camel cigarette, and ate a Hershey bar.

Owen tapped the glass, which by now had dropped only 3/10. He stared at it for a few seconds, weighed its reaction, and then with a shrug, turned back to the wheel. Phil once again studied the chart to renew his recollection of the course lines ahead—though merely as an assurance of something he already knew. It was really a personal wheelhouse habit, which spoke volumes of the man. There was an intense bond between these two men. Each respected the others' particular capability, and each was confident and comfortable in his place in the hierarchy of command. That mutual respect, built on past sea trials they had shared, would last each a lifetime. Now they watched the totality of the sea and sky around them, seeking some glimmer of expectation of the hours that lay dead ahead.

Below, Claude and Kato had cleared the workbench and engine room sole, lashed their dilapidated chair to a station, and locked the Johnson bar in place against the forward bulkhead. The engine room was secure. If it were to happen, the *Doris E.* would be ready for a blow.

To the west, Rose Point on the tip of Graham Island was the last bastion protecting them from what was to come. They passed it in innocence just moments after the bridge clock struck noon.

Some offshore cloud cover began to drape the scene, turning the sky flat gray like a dead bottom cod. With it all, the westerly continued to build, tugging at Phil's halibut jacket, whipping at its corners, and bending the brim of his Sou'wester as he stood outside the wheelhouse, grasping the pipe rail of the bridge and watching the wave tops fracture in the wind.

An hour and a half and fifteen miles north of Point Rose, the wind had shifted to the northwest and was coming now in gusts that raced across a rising sea already roiled with tidal masses. To avoid the hammering of the heavy-beam sea, Owen reluctantly reduced speed and began alternately tacking back and forth, seeking a softer way of going.

There was none, and it had begun to rain. The gulls and their cries had long since gone, soaring downwind to huddle in the safety of a lee shore. Halfway across the hellish place, the untouched coffeepot somehow slipped its moorings and fell from the stove, spilling its mixture of water, coffee grounds, and a single raw egg with a shell across the galley sole. The pot then became a loose cannon, rolling across the sole with a clanging and crashing ten times its size. From below, one heard the sound of other things crashing, banging, and rolling that had never crashed, banged, or rolled before.

The waves had become wind-torn mountains and the *Doris E.* was bathed in sea sweat in her efforts to stay stable. Glazed with spray and pelting rain, she moved as much in the vertical as the horizontal, rolling and pitching without respite in the savagery of the tide and windborne waves, struggling for headway like a swimmer whose arms have become dangerously tired. Alternately, bow up and bow down, she fought the depths, shoveling green water over the wheelhouse, then recovering and rising again and again, shuddering and shaking herself like a wet dog, seeking breath and life from a sea too powerful and too abusive to endure. Black diesel smoke cleared her engine room stack to be instantly vaporized by the feral wind. The noise on all sides immersed the mind in a concert of creaking timbers, crashing swells, and breaking crockery. The counterpoint was the harsh solo of the laboring engine and the goddamn banshee wind that swept across Dall Island and the cape with a seeming intent to destroy everything in sight.

For the first time in his life at sea, Phil Hastin became seasick. Fighting a valiant battle, he finally accepted the inevitable and contributed what was left to leeward. There was ample justification. He was not alone.

In such a passage, time is not reckoned in the integers of passing hours or days. Rather, like life, it is measured in terms of slow and steady progress toward a distant place of promised peace and respite. In such seas, headway seems a cruel myth, and one is prone to believe there will be no ending to the ravages of the journey. The vessel and its crew must reach out to grasp the fact that every turn of the screw brings the craft imperceptibly closer to a place of sought solace and quietude. Without a commitment to that faith, a journey or a life can be likened to the fabled legend of the Flying Dutchman: condemned to sail for eternity through dark and terrible storms, closing on but never reaching the blessed refuge of a safe shore.

There were two more endless hours to be suffered and endured until the wind recanted and softened its anger against the southern hills of Prince of Wales Island. With the welcome lowering of the seas, the cadence of the diesel increased as the *Doris E.*, bent but unbroken, headed up Revillagigedo Channel toward Ketchikan, a town featuring brothels perched on stilts, plenty of whiskey, and a blessed harbor of refuge.

The galley had long before become an affliction of disorder and chaos. Water, ankle deep, sloshed against the bulkheads, and fractured cups and saucers littered the blood-red galley sole. A wayward loaf of white bread, unsliced and sodden, had lost its identity against a table leg while a head of lettuce, falling from some perch, lay in the mess like a child's green rubber ball. The black iron stove had been extinguished in deference to the violence around it; the cross-barred stove top was as cold as a gravestone. Utensils and pots and pans hanging from the bulkheads still swung back and forth in the relative calm of the channel's swell, tracing their faint arcs of wear against the bulkhead's brilliant white background, tolling only an absurd silence, like a church bell without a clapper.

For the *Doris E.* and her crew, the time of need for quiet prayer had passed; the trial was over. She slid smoothly into a barnacled mooring at a fish float near the cannery at Ward Cove. Beneath a clearing evening sky now turning red, the small lights of town winked on, one by one, challenging the coming darkness. It had been, quite simply, the worst weather any of them had seen.

It was a time to be thankful for the *Doris E.* and her way of going, for the through bolts that had held her together, and for the shared intangible spirit that had carried them through what I will forever be convinced was the evil reach of the black cormorant.

journey

This is the morning
I will wrap my arms around and hold close
to feel the heartbeat
of the sun
yet not quite risen.

And I will blow softly into the sweet hollow
of dawning's neck
and smell the sensuous perfume
of rising mists across the waters—
now Maxfield Parrish blue.

The tules turn slowly
from black
to living tawny
and dance to the half-light symphony
of a thousand unseen birds;
while fog drops,
falling from the mast and boom,
beating a gentle drum
to herald this day's being.

The slough mirror of morning is shattered here,
and there—fish on the rise.
And coots,
dreaming of being swans,
paddle in plainness
searching for that magic morsel
that will make them prince or queen.

There is no wind.

The engine splits the magic of today's beginning.
The mast top picks up orange light.
And the gulls,
dull white now instead of black,
rise in a hopeful cordon
to swing back and forth across the sternpost
as we go.

There will be many moods to this day.

I will leave the warm bed of quiet and dawn,
and take you with me.
I want to talk with you until that moment
when today slips on the mantle of the night
and walks away from us
into tomorrow.

We motor through the early morning
in mists that seem ethereal,
the engine, a respirator
keeping a living thing alive
till canvas covers can be dropped
like a pale blue gown
and the breasts of sail
can bid "Good Morning"
to the sun.

Each buoy beckons to another;
and for some little while,
we are contained,
fenced in by carbon steel
and the tall white pipes and iron
of
Pittsburg,
Antioch,
Chipps Island,
Port Chicago.

There is a smoke here,
staining the day with misused watercolors,
white and gray.
And wires,
and tall towers,
and tanks with huge names
that steal virginity from shores
once
breathing
free.

A trial to endure
until we reach the waters of the bay.

And on we go,
beneath a sun that ripens
like October's melon,
drinking dark beer
and eating square-canned brislings
with Norwegian names,
tail and all—
and passing boats.

Boats like seabirds,
white and slender winged,
and boats with rubber tire brows,
broad-shouldered bastards,
smoking diesel cigars
and muscling scows
ten times their size
across the supple waters of our morning world.

Sailing Away - from the Author's Collection

And boats that sleep
tied side by side,
embracing one another,
blushing with age,
iron hearts rusting day by day,
disintegrating in a thrombosis
of time,
of salt,
of wind,
and sea.

Sweater-shedding warmth now.

Skies becoming leaden,
holding in the body heat of earth
and directing ever so gently
that the hour may have come
to give the tiller
to a friend
for just some quiet moments,
and then to close one's eyes
and sleep.

And now awaken to a different drum.
Down the dun slot
of Carquinez,
we change
as the sea changes.
Mainsail up and swelling
with the after breeze that courses
through the Gate.

There is a salt here,
and a bow that yaws and pitches
to the rhythm of the bay.
Lines tighten;
we tighten
and dance
with feet of fifty years and more
to the music
of the yellow afternoon.

The Golden Gate is neither gate nor door.
It is an entrance to a gray womb
to which, for my salvation,
I must
from time to time
return.

Today, the wind does not tip waves with white,
only coastal rollers—
endless, breathing mountains
we must climb,
a sky of lamp black
and library paste
matching the hilly sibling of earth
on which we ride,
an equation
of sameness.

Rain salts and peppers the crests and valleys
of our world
and moods us.

The boat lives and speaks
with many tongues
of this, its native land.
We hear and understand—
none of us a stranger
to the sea.

South brings cold
and wind
and swells—
not insurmountable,
but foot-on-deck-and-wall weather,
with lee rails buried
and a bow that chews at water
and spits it in our faces.

Then in a light,
half day,
half night,
the buoy blinks
with no emotion;
and we round it
for the solace
of that which we have sought—
something ventured,
something gained.

We are home.

There is a quiet in my head,
and as a lover, softly, one time said,
"All my thoughts of you are *up* thoughts:
soaring,
joyous,
free,
and eternal."

And there is a peace
upon my body
and my mind,
which I gratefully accept...
but, in truth,
do not choose to fully comprehend.

Summer home

When I was young, the rain was a sweet and gentle thing to me, and the Harper pier leaned crazily into the wind like some gale-tossed cypress inured by time. It stood on spindly, teredo-ravaged piling—driven too long ago, but a fine place for red cod and blue-bellied bottom fish.

Harper was an old place not deserving the accolade of *village*. It was rather a grouping of elderly souls who seemed to have nowhere else to go. Their young had gone away; and these remnants, with bodies twisted like the shakes on their leaky roofs, shuffled (as necessary) between their crude houses and the ancient

120

clapboard store that supplied their basic needs and wet copies of the ubiquitous *Seattle Times*. The Harper folks were ever so much like orphaned ants seeking sugar, ever mindful of, and distressed by, the pelting storms that seemed their lifelong cross to bear.

It was a strange place for a child to love, but the essence of its rain-stroked summers is as vivid and revered as anything that can be found in the iron-bound chest that is the grail of my remembrances. Our summer home, riddled by the Great Depression and an always-present mortgage, lay a mile south of the store, just off the gravel road to Southworth, which hugged the shore of Puget Sound lest its stony beach might run away.

Bordering the beach and road, thick stands of pine and fir curtained the small plots of land that hid the summer huts huddled beneath them. But like some grade-school bully, the large Jensen Place stood on a clear-cut lot, an aggressive two-story "framer." The owners drove new cars and didn't speak or wave when passing. I didn't like them and took delight in the childhood discovery that despite their grandeur, the smoke from their alder-driven fireplace was identical in color and smell to that coming from the meanest cottage—a basal statement on the equality of men.

Solitude, like the rain, was a gift for me. My days as a twelve-year-old were too filled with the blessings of adventure to be shared with others. Blake Island, sheathed in mystery, stood across the narrow strait. I took "terror strolls" through the woods in which a hundred imaginary grizzlies waited to test the mettle of the pellet pistol and sheath knife that I was never without—and there was the fishing from Harper Pier.

Throughout the rain-pocked summer, the best of times were those hours spent in close communion with the world around me. Home-dug worms, a badly rusted fishing pole, and time—that most precious of possessions—were all that was required to make those fishing hours shining replicas in lifelong memory. The boards of the ancient dock, long since grayed like old men's eyebrows, held slivers that easily pierced the seat of worn-out jeans...one had to be careful when choosing a seat on the hand-hewn twelve-by-twelves that lined the edge of the tilted pier.

But below lay a wonderland. Through water that was as clear as the finest gin, the bottom lay beautifully magnified and speckled by multicolored pebbles and bits of sea frond that danced to the invisible music of the swaying tide. Small crabs and other shelled things moved with the rhythm that had been their constant hymn since the beginning of time...a living landscape of changing color and motion on which was played out a microcosm of birth, life, and dying as great or greater than that of the air breathers—which now peopled a world that had once belonged to these sea creatures alone.

And the ultimate treasure of starry flounder, red Irish lords, kelp greenling, and lingcod were to be hooked and played with breathtaking excitement, and in the end, placed with pride on the straightened black coat hanger that had become my stringer. There was abundance here, plenty to fill the larger black skillet with evening sizzles on the woodstove, and surely enough to be coveted by the large black eyes of our cat called Puss. With great injustice, we did not share with her, fearful of curbing a mouser's appetite for the fat mice that scurried about.

And so it went, those summers of wonder that now, with age, make the heart expand with the pure joy of having lived them. Night came, and with it, sleep, filled with the rich dreams of a child blessed to live by an inland sea of ultimate charm and endless variety. When I was much older, I found the spirit of those times in the words of William Shakespeare:

> *The sun shall not be up so soon as I*
> *to test the fair adventure*
> *of tomorrow.*

Passage to Cape Bingham - Edward C. Larson, 2005

cross sound storm

The remembered storms of yesteryears become intrusive bookmarks in the volumes of our lives. They are treasures to be decanted like a tall shot of single malt on those nights when we find ourselves with only reverie as our silent companion.

Dammit, it's a wondrous thing to be fourteen again. Chichagof Island has opened this young being's heart and mind to the eternal grace of a primal universe filled with unsullied magnificence, verdant earth, and the stunning adventure of a virgin Alaska.

Today, a heavy tempest seems my fare. My mother trembles before a storm. In this gray morning's world, I see many who, like her, would run in terror from the mounting wind. But for the child inside me, this rising rage of weather sings the quarter notes of a blessed cantata. It is the voice of an everlasting soul mate, and I am one with the storm.

Thank God, I find myself different from those others who would flee the seeming anger of this day.

I will hold this gift as long as there are storms to be remembered and a beating heart with which to love them.

Starting at the top, I'll tell you first of the morning sky, given as a gift to me. Were it music, I would hear it as the rising overture to a somber sonata filled with intransigence and sorrow. The covert menace of its wind-torn clouds speaks in the language of intimidation, whispering in my ear, "Best reef in or run under bare poles this day, lad; there's far worse yet to come." The whole of the threat leaves me wide-eyed and breathless while scurrying claws of anticipation run up and down my spine. From the high altar of the blackened sky above me, the distant sound of a kettledrum of thunder rolls down the strait. And then with a single downbeat from the maestro's baton, the rain begins to fall.

Soon enough, it is the wind's turn to lend its raucous voice to the rising choir of this storm-filled morning. The beast this gale will soon become was birthed in those far, dark waters and waves my friends and I call "The Outside"—a place beyond the guardians, the capes known as Cape Spencer and Cape Bingham—a place where one fights great fish, heavy seas, and a pernicious fear. Big Tom, a Tlingit seiner, once told me "The Outside" is the place where Sun sleeps each night, watched over by Raven, the wicked trickster, creator of all things and master of the Sun. Now this far venue is beset by seas as big as buildings and vagrant clouds of darkness. Today, Sun will not rise to spread its yellow warmth across the earth. Instead, it will sleep beneath the covers of its shadowed bed and bower. There will be all hell's fury beyond the capes on this storied morning.

Today, Wind bears the singular malevolence of a hungered wolverine. Filled with unrepentant predation, Wind carries Rain on its back as it slides through the open storm door to freedom. Now it leaps, unfettered, down the strait toward Althorp's dock and the sequestered hiding place I have chosen with such special care. I will be sheltered from the coming rage as I stand in the leeward shadow of a three-pile stanchion of Sitka spruce. The piling is bound together forever with lengths of Roebling steel towing cable. The assemblage is strong enough to lift the sleeping Sun.

From the west, I see Wind and falling sheets of Rain racing toward me. They are the blue-tinged scrims lining the stage for a play that I shall call *Armageddon*. Wind has begun the moaning dirge of the quick and the dead. Roiled waves, harbingers of the coming storm, stretch to the west as far as the eye can see. Now, within this small sphere where I abide, there is a frightening hollowness of fear. In an instant, it will be filled—not with the reality of where and who I am—but rather with the angst and ill-subdued panic that tells me I have perhaps stayed here too long. But the die has been cast. Wind, Rain, and the destiny of this dark morning wrap themselves around me in a tangled mat of terror and stunning exhilaration. I am one with this storm.

A dagger swathed in lightning and roaring of thunder thrusts itself into the top of Salt Chuck Mountain, and the flashing moment becomes quite biblical. I wonder if Saint Peter may have swung the blade.

By age fourteen, I have spent countless Sunday mornings wriggling on a hard oaken church pew, and the congruity of that experience has convinced me there is a God. When I was five or six, I believed the Lord hung out around the Green Lake Congregational Church in my hometown of Seattle. I also suspected He was on very friendly terms with our pastor, the Reverend Lincoln B. Wirt. Although Reverend Wirt never told me that he was buddy-buddy with the Lord, I assumed it to be true because the reverend's sermons took up a great deal of my Sunday mornings. Unfortunately, he never discovered that after the first ten minutes of preaching, seldom a soul is saved!

But as I've grown older, I've begun to suspect that God doesn't reside in Seattle. Instead, He lives beside me here on the shores and upland meadows of this exquisitely beautiful island I have grown to know and love; and seeming to prove my theory that Chichagof Island is truly the Lord's turf, as this deluge begins,

I find myself at the bottom of the largest baptismal font in Christendom as all my sins are washed away in a maelstrom of Port Althorp rain.

Shrieking Wind, now releasing full blows, is infinitely stronger than I imagined it could be. Spreading my hip boots apart, I lean head and shoulders into the storm, grabbing a length of cable to prevent myself from being swept from my perch and blown off the dock. Rain is a twofold menace, totally blinding me at one moment as it falls straight down in a torrential deluge, the next moment, driving horizontally across the windward side, plastering my oilskins to my body. I am a small herring rolled up in a giant sheet of shrink-wrap as rain pellets sting my face with the force of countless silver bullets fired from the vortex of the screaming gale.

The sound of the onslaught is deafening. The numbing downpour beats the corrugated metal roofing of the cannery buildings like some percussion instrument from hell, and the whole earth is a-swing with the raw violence of this stunning spectacle. Millennium trees are rocked to near destruction under the body blows of the assailing elements; and from deep in the forest, I can hear the occasional crash and farewell of a falling giant too weak and too old to face further torment and travail.

Suddenly, a squall scoops up a five-foot cable reel, sending it rolling willy-nilly across the dock just feet from my sanctuary. Picking up speed, the heavy reel slams into the twelve-by-twelve-inch timber bordering the dock where it bounces high into the air and then plunges over the side into the roiled waters of Althorp Bay.

Until this moment, I have been convinced there is little love of spelling or math within me. A child's dusty classroom window has been my vista and the wings of adventure to the world outside; but the crash of the rolling cable reel has stamped an indelible exclamation point across the transfixed stanzas of my consciousness; and I realize I have been daydreaming here, beneath this storm, just as I have often daydreamed while gazing through the dingy pane of my fifth-grade window!

My sainted grandmother taught me to look beyond my eyes. She taught me well; and once taught, we dreamed our dreams together. Here, my dreaming time has turned inward upon itself, like a sock turned inside out...at once becoming a yin and yang, leaving one without an end or a beginning. There is no index, no dibble stick to tell me how long I have languished in this rain and wind. *Has it rained forever? Or have I simply rooted here to become an intrinsic part of this living rainforest that has totally engulfed my mind, my spirit, and even time itself?*

Rain gushes forth with no surcease from the avenging Raven. The huge dock has become a flawless mirror of wetness fit to reflect all the anger and grayness of heaven's totality. The small beasts of the soaking forest will be seeking shelter with a desperation akin to survival, and the brown bears' tiny progeny will rest in warmth and dryness against the underbellies of the fearsome carnivores with which we share this wildness.

Finally, far to the west, beyond Dad Rock and Three Hill Island, a slender needle of silver sky whispers a curtain call to the legerdemain of Raven and a wake-up call to sleeping Sun. Exhausted and out of breath, Wind gives up the day, and Rain slinks off to wherever it flows. The sweet vapor of immaculate salt air lightly fogs this universe; and the margins of the bay become clear, succinct, and bathed in breathless beauty.

Scanning the pier toward the north, I see the *Doris E.* slack-tied with her slip lines resting against the face of the dock. She will be one of a handful of vessels whose memory will sail with me as long as there is an ocean to cross. A true towboat, she is eighty-five feet on deck with a high wheelhouse, a Bristol heart, and a diesel engine the size of a locomotive. Abaft the port side davits, her galley stack puffs out a slim column of donut smoke. Fred Foster, her aged cook, will be making "ringers" for an afternoon coffee session. In boat parlance, we call it a "mug-up."

I run up the stairs to our quarters above the company stores, walk in, and immediately catch hell from my mother for standing out in the driving rainstorm. Beneath my oilskins, my new red Pendleton shirt is soaked from the recent adventure. As she has done a hundred times before, my mother simply shakes her head in wonder and concern, then turns and walks away.

That afternoon, in a dry shirt, I take my rifle and hike toward Round Island at the head of the bay. In deference to a huge population of Alaskan brown bears, I walk carefully, close to the tide line as I have been taught, staying as far as I can from the heavy tree and brush line bordering the wide gravel beach. A bear confrontation, always a possibility on our island, would be totally one-sided. My small-bore rifle serves only as a companion, not a means of defense. My mother adamantly refuses to allow me to carry an adequate weapon; and at fourteen, I prefer not to question her logic, which, in its way, is slightly troubling. If in a fair fight, on whose side would she be? *Mine? Or the bear's?*

The morning's storm has scoured the forest and bay to visual perfection. Where the sky remains a threatening gray, it is crisscrossed now by herring gulls whose whiteness matches the virginal hue of a store-bought wedding gown.

My path winds past large clumps of bull kelp covered en masse by sand flies. Across the shining beach gravel, small crabs and other tiny misplaced souls have been cast up by wind and waves. The whole of my world is saturated by the elemental perfume of forest and sea.

I walk perhaps a half mile and then stand at the edge of Margaret Creek, still running vigorously with the effects of the morning's storm. The creek will not be low enough to fish for at least a day. Dolly Varden trout lurk in the deep riffles downstream from the granite boulders lining her way. This afternoon, she is all white water. Tomorrow with the torrent gone, she will run in the rich and wondrous amber of Matisse, clear as gin, brutally cold, and sweet to fish. Twenty yards downstream, where she pours herself into the bay, a huge pool forms a playground for a dozen river otters flashing through the water with the speed of light. Perhaps I can fish my favorite hole tomorrow or the day after that. Early darkness now creeps down the mountainsides. It's time to go home.

I don't recall looking back at the creek and its amber waters again. I only recall it fading into silence as I walked away. That may be just as well. My Tlingit Raven from beyond the capes had already decreed that I would never again fish Margaret Creek…at least not in this eternity. Surely Poe's Raven had the last word when he quipped, "Nevermore."

It was only three weeks following my trek to Margaret Creek that I was awakened from a deep sleep by the midnight howl of the cannery's steam whistle. As quickly as possible, I threw on a Pendleton and pair of cords. Rushing into our living room, I discovered my dad already dressed and my mother in her robe.

As the three of us stood staring in alarm at each other, a huge explosion blew the immense doors off the cannery building far out across the dock. The blast, only thirty feet from our living room, left us stunned. The fire raged all night with the flames rising to meet the dawn hovering over Dish Mountain. The cannery at Port Althorp had simply ceased to exist.

The last smoke arising from the burned ruins carried with it my family's lifestyle and good fortune. They blew away toward the capes and vanished in the morning air, far out where Raven rules the Sun.

And still another sorrow. In the hands of unknown incompetents, my beloved towboat, the *Doris E.*, would suffer an engine-room fire and find her grave on a graveled shoal in the Alaska that had birthed her spirit.

Wars came and went, as did the years between. It would be sixty-some years before I returned to Margaret Creek—not to fish Dolly Varden, but to spread my mother's ashes in the amber otter pool we had both loved so much.

The beach is still marred by the flames of long ago, but if one looks out toward the open sea, the glory of this place shines on. Today, simply recalling my time here opens up billions of pixels in my mind; and I am young again, loving every facet of what I once was.

Someday, I will again stand there.

Joyfully.

In a yellow slicker.

And I will watch a new storm drive in from The Outside.

From the place of the Raven where the Sun sleeps.

Yes Bay - Edward C. Larson, 2005

hell for stout

From a lofty point, I can look back across the days of
my years and pick out a few memorable moments of
"excitement-love-terror-action" that have made my life
really worth living. One such memory, still revered and
clear after more than fifty years, regards a boat I used
to know. I'd like to tell you about her.

My father began a career in the Alaska salmon
fishing business in 1908. As I grew up, he occasionally
regaled me with stories of a dinosaur cannery tug called
the *Yes Bay*, named after a small harbor in southeastern
Alaska. She was ancient when Dad first went north,
and I suspect she was probably "birthed" sometime in

the early 1880s. Originally powered by steam, she was re-engined about 1900 with a huge, primitive Metz & Weiss diesel, often referred to by my dad as "that goddamn rats-and-mice engine." It was hard to start and showered the boat and crew with huge chunks of carbonized fuel every time she was cranked up.

The *Yes Bay* was built "hell for stout," with huge oak ribs and planking for the ages. She was built with hand saws and a brace and bit you turned with the power in your arms. Tall and ungainly, even a clipper bow didn't lend her any grace. She was a bag woman of a boat, but I'm sure of one thing: one night while she was on the ways, an eternal soul crept aboard her to nest forever down among her bilge timbers. I'll swear to that, and you'll soon learn why.

While I was still in grade school, my dad took me to Alaska in the summers to work on the cannery tugs. I accomplished a lot in those formative years, learning to cuss in fluent Norwegian and finding out what beer and dirty jokes were all about. Dad's company had bought the *Yes Bay*, and she was part of the scene while I was growing up. They didn't pay much for her, but then they didn't get a hell of a lot of boat, either...at least so they thought.

My Alaska summers were idyllic, stretching through my high school years until that fateful December in 1941 when the whole world changed, and I went away, flew airplanes, and came back in one piece after three and a half years of war.

In 1947, I headed once more for Alaska, working for my uncle on a relatively new cannery tender call the *Golden West*. Our cannery was located on Prince of Wales Island, one of God's garden places, located off the coast of southern Alaska not far from Ketchikan. The site was a forested, pristine paradise; but as is often the case, beauty belies danger. The southern end of the island terminates in a vicious bit of ocean at Dixon's Entrance. At this spot, tidal bores bearing down from Cordova Bay meet the great swells sweeping in from the North Pacific and turn the area into a welter of raging ocean. In heavy southwesterly storms and in boats smaller than an ocean liner, the place is simply life-threatening.

After a big salmon season, we were towing a barge back to the cannery. As I recall, it was late on a Friday when we noticed the glass beginning a rapid fall. Choosing discretion rather than valor, our skipper, Norman Varro, decided to anchor the *Golden West* and our tow in a small protected bay north of the cape and out of harm's way. With pinochle and strong coffee, our crew of five waited to see what the weather would do.

That year, there was a heavy run of late king salmon, magnificent Chinooks weighing thirty to forty pounds. A great number were iced at the cannery and packed into large wooden boxes for transport to Ketchikan, a hundred miles away around the cape. Unbeknownst to us, the *Yes Bay* had departed the cannery the day before on a "milk run" to deliver a deck load of the iced Chinooks to Ketchikan for the waiting restaurant trade. She had plodded along through the night, passing our refuge before dawn, and with the deck load piled high had rounded the cape and turned northeast under heavy weather into a howling southwesterly gale.

An hour into dawn, we heard a desperate call from her skipper. The lashings had broken, and the deck load had shifted to starboard, creating a severe list, which threatened to sink her. The heavy boxes had become "loose cannons," smashing into her gunwales, then splintering into pieces. The skipper of the *Yes Bay* also advised that an aging deck hand had passed out and was comatose on the wheelhouse floor, barely breathing from a suspected heart attack.

Before the message was finished, Virgil Schmoetzer, our engineer, dashed below to start the engine, and Varro ordered me forward to raise the anchor. The tow was secured; and in minutes, with the throttle lever to the stops, we were making it for Cape Chacon.

Through the spray and rain, we saw the *Yes Bay* first from about a half mile away, perhaps eight to ten miles northwest of the cape. The weather was as vicious as I had seen. Wind tore off the wave tops, hurling them against the wheelhouse, threatening to smash in the windows. Visibility was so bad the windows were lowered part way; and in seconds, we were soaked. Seawater was sloshing back and forth athwartships across the wheelhouse deck. We had taken water from the beam seas, and the galley aft of the wheelhouse could best be described as a *sonofabitch*!

As we closed within two hundred yards to lee of the *Yes Bay*, it was obvious her situation was desperate. My vision of her is as clear today as it was then: she was wallowing in a maelstrom of sea. Her deck load had shifted, and she was listing severely to starboard. The water around her was littered with hundreds of heavy wooden salmon boxes—some intact and some broken into splinters—with the large iced Chinooks floating around them. Many of the cases had lodged crazily against the *Yes Bay*'s starboard railings, a logjam of weight that was beginning to turn her over. Seas were breaking over her stern; and now large steel drums aft of her cabin had broken loose and were rolling side to side, threatening to crush anything in their way.

It was obvious she had to execute a 180-degree turn and head back whence she came, but the timing for the turn would be absolutely critical. To save the boat, she had to be brought about between swells. Varro and the other skipper confirmed the plan by radio, and we pulled up two hundred yards windward to stand by and offer whatever small shelter we could.

Schmoetzer was standing by in our engine room; Bob Ericksen, our cook, was in the galley attempting to salvage some order from the welter of pots and pans and crockery that now littered the galley floor. Varro, our skipper; Karl, the second deck hand; and I were glued to the half-open windows of the wheelhouse, drenched with seawater, and immersed in a drama we could scarcely believe. We waited for one minute. Then two. Then perhaps three or four, searching the mountainous sea for any semblance of momentary calm — then it seemed there was a slight flattening, and the Yes Bay began her struggle to turn and survive.

The skipper had put her helm far over to lessen the turning time; and she began to swing, her rails under water from the weight of the cases jammed against her starboard gunwale. She had turned 90 degrees when a huge crest rolled under the Golden West and rushed ahead to hit the Yes Bay full abeam. It seemed a body blow she couldn't withstand. The full force of the breaking wave rolled the stricken boat upright then full over on her port side. The remaining heavy salmon cases cascaded across her near-vertical deck into a welter of foam and debris, and the oil drums astern smashed into her port gunwales and bounced overboard.

The sight would be carved forever in the minds of the three of us who watched. There were no words as the clipper bow of the Yes Bay rolled under and raised her stern clear of the water. For a seemingly endless time, she posed there with her huge green-yellow propeller slowly churning the air, while her mast and boom, mounted forward, laid on the passing swell like a head on a pillow. I saw the encrusted bottom of her rudder and skeg and knew she was going down.

For perhaps thirty seconds, she lay on the surface like a dead bird, rolling in the debris of her own making: gutted salmon, smashed boxes, floating bits of line, rusted tin cans, and I could see the floating oak bucket that had held her heaving line. In the midst of the violence of the place, these moments seemed a noiseless, breath-holding time…a waiting…waiting.

Then came the miracle.

The *Yes Bay's* stern lowered slowly into the water where it belonged, and her huge propeller once more began turning the water into a green-whiteness. She shook and rose very slowly like the bag woman she was, wallowed about, and finished the turn, slowly creeping back toward us and safety. Her decks were swept clean, shedding cascades of white water beam to beam, while black smoke and cinders trailed from her stack and vanished into the wind.

For the next two hours, we crawled together back to the safety of the bay. In the plan of things, it was hard to define who was saved and who was savior.

Everything else was anticlimactic.

The engine room on the *Yes Bay* had shipped two feet of water, but the old "rats-and-mice" diesel had a pressurized base, and the engine probably would have continued banging away totally submerged and upside down. The galley, a shambles, was set right again after a few hours of brooming and mopping had filled a GI can with broken crockery and wet playing cards. Two portside four-by-four oak strakes had snapped off when the oil drums went over the side, but other than drying out, the *Yes Bay* was little the worse for wear.

The ailing deck hand had indeed been unconscious, but only from the effects of severe seasickness, and he recovered after a day's rest in the quiet backwater of the small bay. If memory serves me, both the *Golden West* and the *Yes Bay* were back in harness by

Monday; and two weeks later, we were headed south for Seattle and a winter's rest.

I went north the following year for the last time. The idyllic chapters of my Alaskan summers closed with a grateful epilogue.

In the cold light of reason, it seems ridiculous to accede life to a creature of wood, steel, and nails, but it's fun for me to speculate about the *Yes Bay* and the eternal soul that I'm sure lies within her.

It's been nearly fifty years since that savage morning on Cape Chacon. The *Yes Bay* is probably gone now, but don't bank on it. I'm sure I could investigate, but I'd rather remember her in that moment of triumph, rising like a phoenix out of the cold waters of the cape, shaking herself off, and heading for home.

I think you'd like to remember her that way, too.

A wind has blown the rain away
and blown the sky away
and all the leaves away...

· e. e. cummings ·

plowed under

The hearts of some few men I know
are star-crossed with soaring wings of birds.
In quiet reverie, their footsteps tread
the leaf-strewn paths of yesterday—
brushing at once the grasses of the plain
and the flower carpet of the morning meadow.

There is no wire in their worlds.
They are men out of time
whose souls, like their footsteps,
cross the peaceful silence of eventides now forgotten—
and who walk in truth and dignity
a trail, long since, plowed under.

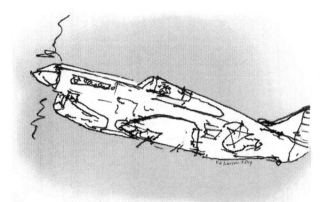

Fighter - Edward C. Larson, 2014

remembering yunnanyi

Yunnanyi. It seems almost impossible that more than seventy years have slipped by since a great war began to stop. Oh, a good look in the mirror confirms it all right; I'm what many people call an "old man," but there's some joy in the fact that my memories tell me it wasn't always this way. Maybe that's why old guys like me spend a lot of time remembering.

There wasn't much going on around the house the other day, and the dishes were done, so out of boredom or nostalgia, I set out to reconstruct what I was doing on VE Day 1945. My research began with a stack of old letters, lovingly saved and bound with twine by my mother, who left some time ago. Untouched for years, they were yellow, smelled moldy, and spoke volumes of other places and other times. Next, I went through my flight log, which offered some clues and jogged an aging memory. After putting two and two together, I was able to pretty well confirm the events of that day and how they affected a twenty-year-old Army Air Forces pilot, dangling from the marionette strings of fate in a place he never dreamed he'd ever see or be.

I don't believe we even got the news about VE Day till later...maybe the next day. After all, that war was half an earth away, and news traveled relatively slowly in those days—especially to a lovely but primitive valley set in the backwater of war in western China. Yunnanyi was the name of the place. It was just east of the Burmese border and totally overshadowed by the rising mass of the Himalayas, the infamous "Hump," which crunched up to scary heights and rubbed the skies to the north and west of our airstrip. The valley, its rice paddies, and its people had been there forever. The Americans who flew airplanes there for a while were only a catch in its breath.

If there were a reason for our being there (which I constantly doubted), it was to fly gasoline, bombs, and ammunition to the fighter squadrons that were harassing what was left of the Japanese forces farther to the east. Our lives were filled with indolence, not by choice but by fate. We waited around and flew when ordered...sort of outcasts. We were "spear-carriers" in the stage play of World War II, a war that

Ed and Pete - from the Author's collection, 1945

swirled dramatically around every place but where we were. If we didn't know the scenario, we knew the players. They were guys whom we envied, guys that we flew with, trained with, and who found themselves in the forefront of the war flying B-17s over Schweinfurt, or Mustangs and Thunderbolts over the Solomons or Iwo Jima. We were just hanging out in a valley as old as time, while stuff went on all around us.

With us, there was never the dignity of having your own plane and painting your girl's name on the nose. We used whatever would run at the time, and whatever was loaded and assigned for that trip. Our planes had no names, only unromantic four-digit numbers painted somewhere on their scarred carcasses. Some were war-weary B-24 bombers turned into trucks by having their guts removed. And then there were asthmatic old C-46s and C-47s that wheezed and coughed when you asked them to climb higher than the mountains that surrounded us. There were of course differences in them, like the differences one might find between a good horse and a bad horse; but by and large, they all had pretty much the same decrepit feel.

If you were flying, you always preflighted the airplane. That was, you walked around outside it and looked to see if the propellers were fastened on and if most of the bolts still had nuts on them. Then you climbed up a shin-busting ladder and sort of crawled and hunched over and squeezed to get in, always hitting your head on something made of aluminum.

Flight Training - from the Author's Collection, 1944

LT. EDWARD CHARLES LARSON, AGE 20
"THE YOUNGEST PILOT IN THE CHINA-BURMA THEATRE"
- from the Author's Collection, 1945

The cockpit or flight deck was always the same. It was a "used" place smelling of hydraulic oil, aviation gasoline, and sweat. There was ever-present dirt, grit on the floor, and maybe an empty Lucky Strike cigarette package crammed down in a cranny by the rudder pedals. These planes were like gas station restrooms in a bad part of town. There was no ownership; and nobody ever cleaned up the place, like maybe it was supposed to be unlucky. If there was fabric anywhere, it was threadbare, and the steering wheel on the control yoke was black and kind of sticky. Actually, it was covered with a patina of ten thousand sweaty palms flying through hours of boredom or moments of terror.

In spots, the instrument panels were worn to bare metal by time, the stare of a thousand eyes, and the constant throwing of switches or pulling of levers by the guys that flew in this tiny space. Paint was worn and chipped; and plastic knobs had lost the newness of the red, green, and yellow that sort of reminded you what this thing or that thing did. Plexiglas windows were often crazily cracked here or there, and wind came in around the edges. The ashtrays were always full; and I suppose if you stretched your imagination, you could pick up the scent of a mixture of adventure and fear that was a part of this scruffy space.

On the day in question—and I'm pretty sure I'm right—somebody and I flew a load of aviation gasoline to where the action was, a little town called Chihkiang, a couple of hours to the east. The home field at Yunnanyi was 6500 feet high, and I remember we had a tough time getting the old C-46 "unstuck" on takeoff. There were a lot of fifty-gallon drums aboard, tied down of course. As far as I know, nobody ever understood how to check the weight and balance of the airplane...there was some fancy slide rule thing, which we were always losing. In this case, we were probably overloaded. It was a unique experience to sit there with the engines roaring, running out of time and runway in an airplane that felt like a flyable lump of coal. Needless to say, we made it; and after a couple of hours, two or three cigarettes, and an approach with full flaps, we landed at Chihkiang on a strip that I always felt was too narrow and too short.

At Chihkiang, the Japanese were so close that our Mustang fighter planes were strafing ground troops almost before they got their wheels off the ground. Japanese snipers were always sneaking around and shooting at stuff. One of our guys got a rifle bullet through both knees while he was sitting in the cockpit running up the engines before takeoff. After that, we were careful where we ran up the engines; and if it was night, we left the cockpit lights off.

It didn't take long to offload. It was simply a matter of rolling barrels to the doorway and letting 'em drop eight feet or so on to rubber tires. We had lunch and a smoke and always strolled around and looked at the *real* airplanes sitting there...late-model Thunderbolts and lovely P-51 Mustangs that we would never fly. It was always like looking at a Ferrari while you were driving a garbage truck. That day, there was an

With us, there was never the dignity
of having your own plane
and painting your girlfriend's name on the nose.

C-46 Diner, Yunnanyi, China - Edward C. Larson, 2014

We used whatever would run at the time.

unexciting return to Yunnanyi—it was usually like that unless the weather was bad. I think one of the engines developed bad magnetos on the way back; and when we told the crew chief, he got mad as hell at the prospect of having to take the damn thing apart.

We lived in tents. About fifteen feet square. To make them more inhabitable, we built wooden walls four feet high and raised the tents up on top of them. That gave us more headroom; and we could have a stove inside, which made it more comfortable since it really got cold in the winter months at that altitude. We also stretched strips of airplane tire inner tubes across wooden frames, making really great mattresses. Although it didn't look like much, with a wooden floor and the charcoal stove, it was home.

As a pastime, we made primitive radios out of razor blades, pencil lead, and cardboard tubing wrapped with wire…like old crystal sets. There was always a lot of arguing over whose could play the loudest. One guy sent home for a real crystal and beat all the competition. All we had to listen to was the transmitter out of a crippled airplane that broadcasted Glenn Miller music and some Dorsey and Artie Shaw. It was kind of nuts, but those little radios were really important at the time, and the music was about all the entertainment we had.

I can imagine after the trip, we went down to the flight surgeon's quarters and got the two-ounce shot of whiskey we were entitled to after every flight. If you saved up sixteen chits, they'd give you a full bottle. For me, the booze was like candy, and I never managed to save any chits. On days we didn't fly, we made picture frames out of Plexiglas or checked out the rifle and went hunting for pheasant up in the hills. We read a lot, smoked a lot, thought about sex a lot, cursed a lot, flew a little, and waited for the war to end.

I'm sure we didn't make too much fuss about VE Day, though maybe we should have. We still had a little war going on where we were. It lasted long enough around Yunnanyi so that Herb Briggs, Tony Baldasare, and Junior Monahan didn't come home with us. I remember them. And I remember the pristine beauty of the high meadows around the strip and the sight of figures as old as time, bent to their tasks in the rice paddies.

A lot of other stuff I have forgotten.

I suspect that when the last engine sound faded from the valley, the reality of our being there went away—as it should have. I hope the quiet cadence of centuries past returned and brought peace to the place once more. The Li River ran not too far from the valley. I understand it's a must for tourists now, along with the beehive hills around Guilin. We used to buzz the green loveliness of those hills all the time—and caught hell for it. When we flew real low, white birds, like egrets, would rise to the engine noise. It was beautiful...and sort of poetic.

I still walk the place in memories. But I don't think I want to go back.

There are too many years in between.

bangalore

The dust of eons clouds my footprints.
The heat of a just-born dawn
    foretells the crucible of noon.

Bangalore lies like a dung cake
    burning in the sun.

The ears become awash in tongues
    of Urdu and Tamil,
    the Dravidian singsong of a dynasty.
The chorus swells
    with the flute of screeching cart wheels
    wanting grease.

The violins, a cat screaming for sinister reasons—
a synergistic symphony of squalor and despair.
My senses fill from the assault of a thousand sights
and sounds.

Chalk-white hovels spotted with black doorways
and faces of mahogany:
toothless specters,
vase-headed,
bearing fouled water
for the bellies of their babies;
the rotting leper with mattered eyes
beseeches coins
and turns my gaze aside.

The fetid air is layered with the stench of ages.
A nostrum of unwashed bodies
and polyglot sewage
floods the gutter beside my sandaled stride
and swills the pigs nearby.

The smell of life and stink of death
is powdered and preened
by patchouli oil burning in the sun.

The mouth, guarded by close-set teeth
and tight-pressed lips, is violated by the day.
Unwillingly, it tastes the dead burning
on the river *ghats*
and seeks to extricate itself
through spittle on the dusty ground.
The spots of darker tan vanish in the sun.

Fishing in the Rain - Edward C. Larson, 1992

Atoms of lotus float across

still waters

The phantom green of newborn rice
  stretches across the valleys of my view
  and seams the hem of a dress
  worn by the purple hills of Kerala.

I hear the cry of weaver birds
  and the wing stroke of a swan
  rising against the morning mists.

Atoms of lotus float across still waters;
  and I taste the overture of morning,
  while Bangalore lies like a dung cake
  burning in the sun.

hong kong

Hong Kong. Sunday.

Time, people, places, and things.

It starts early—eyes and ears awaken to the smell of China.

Framed by my rusting metal window sash, the green hills shed their drifting clouds and, wiping their eyes with verdant sleeves, awake to a Sunday morning sun.

But not quite all at once.

There is still sleep in the streets—and the early working destitute, sitting on a red chipped stool, folds morning papers and in defiance (all that's left) bars the sweeper's way.

There is a texture to the Kowloon morning streets, a patina of trash, forlorn hope, and hurry, as well as light and shadow, urine, and the ages.

I walk in a city of high-rise shadows. Buildings grow from gardens much too small for them—pot-bound plants searching for the sun. Some are marked with a bamboo gossamer of scaffolding—a tender travesty on which workmen climb toward the clouds to make their concrete branches reach even higher and thus give life to what's below.

The city, like the hills, is wiping the sleep from its eyes—and the voice of a thousand trucks and buses bids good morning to the building-shaded streets. They scurry through the damp of the day's beginning like earthbound insects slowly devouring the quiet and peace of Sunday's birth.

But it is a decent time for awakening, and soon a teeming multimillion feet will blanket the streets and alleys of this alien place. They will awaken to the same sea, sun, and air—the common commodity—the destitute, prostitute, and affluent.

The legless one, dragging on filthy, padded stumps, sullies the Union Jack façade of the Peninsula Hotel—that bastion of tenuous strength standing by the will of God and Mao Tse-tung—where one can mingle in incestuous sociability and ignore the real world revolving in the streets outside. But no rancor here—apparently those inside do not want out, and those outside do not want in.

The outside people spice my day.

The ferry, "Morning Star," rumbles and rocks across the morning shine of Victoria Harbour. I disembark and walk to the tram, which lifts me on a tender tether to the clouds. Viewed from above, the minor tawdriness of the city pales, and the jewel is in its setting—an eye-blinding, mind-expanding composite of time and space and loveliness.

The harbor is a pond of magic green with "lily pad" freighters and junks and tugs—water skippers hastening to the four compass corners of the world. It is a surfeit of view—awe-striking, shimmering in the yellow haze of sunlit fog that, like me, is reluctant to leave or turn the eye away.

An adventure and feast over, the tram threads down the warming hillside. Only a short walk to Charta Park and the people—a potpourri of ten thousand to the square mile. Exotic people reveling in the yellow warmth that paints the bay and hills. Wan Chai street girls with the ultradelicacy of the young and beautiful—with skin tones of warm brass and soft, yellowed copper. Bodies, faint-breasted and exquisitely desirable in Bang-Bang T-shirts and Lee jeans. And the children—hair black and shining—wide-eyed, fresh, and scurrying across the cultivated grass.

There is a cohesion and acceptance of this lot upon this day of rest and play. When night falls, they will turn back to the dingy tackiness of soot-stained high rises and dream of wonders that this day has brought.

And I will wonder, too—to find so easily, as a stranger, the warmth and loveliness, the delicacy, and triumph of a people penned by sea and hills, whose children, love, and laughter bring the sunlight to Charta Park on Sunday afternoon.

82ND Airborne - Edward C. Larson, 2017

night flight

The long shadows of late October fell across the deserted anchorage as Paul Groszman locked the wheelhouse door on the fishing schooner *Tuna*. The fishing boat, anchored seventy-five yards from the pier in Santa Cruz, California, was his pride, his life, and his livelihood. The days of his years had failed to lavish many gifts on Paul; what he had, he'd earned.

He had no problem with that.

His days as a fisherman began before dawn and lasted often into darkness, not unlike others who chose to reap an elusive bounty from the land or sea. Almost daily fishing trips to the cod grounds around

Año Nuevo Island had furnished Paul, Helen, and the kids with a decent if not expansive lifestyle for a lot of years. It was enough.

He winced as he climbed into the small skiff and rowed slowly toward the wharf. This afternoon, he had changed spark plugs in the old Chrysler engine, and his back hurt—*bad!* There was something insidious, threatening about the pain he had known for months. It was like a sinister knocking on the door of his life—as if something bad wanted to come in, and it worried him.

Pain was no stranger to Paul. As a child on a volunteer errand for his widowed mother, there had been a heavy rain and a serious cycle accident that left him with a fractured skull and severe concussion. The recovery had demanded intensive nursing care and had stolen a year from his childhood. He emerged from the trauma with a maturity that belied his years and a capacity to accept and deal with adversity. These were traits that would serve him well in the years ahead. Paul's father had died a year before the accident. He had been a highly respected educator, dealing with handicapped children, and had instilled in his son a deep sense of compassion and dedication to the needs of others. It was a principle Paul Groszman never forgot.

Nineteen fifty-three had been a good year for cod and salmon, but the fallow time for fishing had arrived. In a week or perhaps two at the most, the southeast winds would begin to blow, and the anchorage would become a dangerous and impossible place.

His was the only boat left. The others, like weary bears, had crept away for a winter's hibernation in safe harbors at Moss Landing or across the bay. A few old Monterrey hulls, the bright paint of spring now faded, hung from the davits on the wharf, swaying in the wind like ancient Christmas ornaments. Everything else was gone—the boats, the crowds, and the sunlit days of summer. By staying, he had taken a chance and made a few bucks.

Now the time had come to leave.

That morning, he had taken a group north to the island and on the return had sensed the coming of winter: long, heavy swells, mountains of water rolling in from their birthing place three thousand miles at sea. There were still some blues and greens left in the water world, but it would all turn to gray and violence soon enough. Perhaps in the winter resting time, the pain in his back would go away.

Tying the skiff to the landing, he turned once to check the *Tuna* rolling gently in the evening swell; then turning back, he climbed slowly to the pier.

The lights of Stagnaro's Fish Market were a beacon in the gathering darkness of the wharf. Malio, scion of the Stagnaro family, and Paul had developed a deep and lasting friendship. Several years before, they had teamed up to save three of Malio's charter boats from drifting into destruction on the beach in a vicious and unexpected summer storm. Paul was the quintessential nonhero. It was typical of him to act with haste and responsibility in an emergency. It was the only lifestyle he knew. That experience and a mutual love of fishing and the sea had produced a bond between these two men that would last their lifetimes.

Over a beer, Paul talked with Malio about fish and coming storms. They both knew the violence of the *chubasco*, a sudden wind that would leave boats broken and rusting on the beach. The two parted in the thickening darkness and a mild evening breeze. On the way to the car, Paul made the decision to move the *Tuna* south on Sunday—she was a good rig, and he'd hate like hell to lose her.

On the short ride home, the radio crackled with news of the withdrawal of UN forces in Korea. The armistice had been signed at Panmunjom in July, only months before. With the death of Stalin and a new group in power in the Kremlin, it seemed there was a substantial chance for peace. During the war, Paul had visited the naval air base, using the *Tuna* as a shore taxi for visiting naval vessels and attending training classes at the small naval radar station located high in the hills behind town. From its cypress-shaded vantage point, the radar station monitored the movement of ships and aircraft in the Monterrey Bay area. An anachronism now that the war was over, it would be dismantled in the coming year.

The wheels brushed the curb as Paul parked in the darkness of his quiet street. The wind was dying and moved only the lightest branches of the pine by the sidewalk. Startled by the noise of his footsteps, Helen's cat crossed the porch in a single bound as Paul climbed the wooden steps and entered the house.

During dinner, Helen mentioned the call from Connie. She had checked in "to see how things were." Connie, their eldest daughter, was married to Jack Buchholtz, a local policeman. He would work that night on the four till midnight shift. On his days off, Jack worked on the boat with Paul and crewman Harlow Webber. If the salmon or cod run was particularly heavy, it took all three to handle the tasks aboard the forty-two-foot *Tuna*.

After dinner, Paul relaxed in an old overstuffed chair. The nagging pain in his back was still there, like a shadow. He flipped on the radio close at hand and listened to the evening news. There was more about the postarmistice activity near the Chosin Reservoir. Because of his affiliation with the naval air base, he had identified strongly with the war in Korea and was deeply disappointed at its inconclusive finish. He reckoned there would be more trouble in Southeast Asia before too many years had passed.

It was after nine o'clock when Paul showered, bid Helen goodnight, and slid into bed. After reading for a few minutes, he dozed off; and at ten o'clock, he gave up and switched off the reading lamp. Within minutes, he was sound asleep.

There was to be one primal force, one magnificent obsession in the life of Stephen Dutton Jr.—airplanes! Born a year before the crash on Wall Street, he was the only son of a Des Moines, Iowa, hardware dealer—a bright and appealing kid.

The family weathered the Depression better than most, but the reality of the breadlines in the thirties matured Stephen and the nation far beyond their years. He grew up learning that a dime was good pay for mowing a very large lawn.

When the boy was seven, his father paid a friend five dollars to fly Steve around the airport in an ancient Waco biplane. His mother complained bitterly at the danger and expense; but on that day, young Steve had found his future. From that time on, he spent hours in the basement assembling airplane models of delicate balsa wood and rice paper and devouring flying magazines and movies at a truly remarkable pace. The fascination grew with the rich aerial tableau of World War II rolling before the eyes of the bright and impressionable adolescent. The die was cast. Stephen Dutton Jr. would fly.

Stephen did well at James Madison High School, and a paper route paid for some flying lessons in a Piper Cub. In 1949, following graduation from Iowa State with a degree in engineering, he joined the Naval Air Forces; and in the fall of 1951, he was commissioned an ensign in the United States Navy. The dream had come full circle. The years had handed Steve a double-decker prize of achievement and satisfaction. Married and with a two-year-old son, his life was the fulfillment of his childhood imaginations. He loved what he did, and he was very good at it.

In June 1953, Steve, now a lieutenant junior grade (LTJG) officer, was assigned to the US Navy Air Base at Moffett Field, California. He, his wife Barbara, and their young son found comfortable quarters in the married officers' compound; and Steve became a valued member of the Composite Squadron VC-3, flying the last of the great propeller-driven Navy fighters, the F4U Corsair.

The Corsair was a big, cranky airplane — five tons of speed, power, and lethal capability. Still alive in the age of jets, its genesis stretched back through World War II to a 1940 drawing board. A scourge to the Japanese in the Pacific, it had survived because it was a successful weapon as well as a machine of uncommon beauty. Squadron VC3 used the Corsair to develop the night-fighting tactics needed to cope with the new age of flying men and machines. Aerial combat was in a state of flux. Helmets and goggles had been relegated to museums, sacrificed at the altar of speeds faster than sound and technologies that would eventually put men on the moon.

Tonight Steve and two squadron mates would fly a three-plane intercept mission intended to identify, track, and close on target planes posing as enemy patrol bombers. It would be a short exercise of moderate sophistication designed to hone aerial defense skills in the hope they would never be needed. Night fighting demanded an intricate blend of men and machines. Dutton and the Corsair were a matched pair.

The three aircraft, crouching like huge benign insects, awaited their pilots on a taxi strip a quarter mile from the operations building. When the pilots arrived, the engine cowlings were still warm from a preflight run-up an hour before, but the cockpit canopies were misted by a thin fog blowing in like gossamer from the Golden Gate, forty miles away to the north and west.

At a quarter to ten, Steve and his wingmen taxied to the active runway and parked diagonally to accomplish their pretakeoff checklist.

Ten minutes later, the three-ship element lined up on Runway One-Seven, and Dutton received clearance for takeoff. The three pilots advanced throttles in unison; and forty seconds later, they were airborne, gear up, and the lights of Sunnyvale were vanishing in the misty darkness of the night.

They crossed Palo Alto at four thousand feet, climbing into a sky that was darker than it should be. It was exactly ten o'clock—the same moment Paul Groszman in Santa Cruz had chosen to dim his reading lamp and fall asleep.

Crossing the coast at San Gregorio, they leveled off at twelve thousand feet and swung northward toward the Farallon Islands. The night sky and sea blended into a blue-black void, unrelieved by a single light—a journey through a tunnel of darkness with no end or beginning. There was little radio talk among the three, only that which was essential to the completion of the mission. Reaching the Farallones, the initial point of their search, they turned southeast and switched on their radar sets to detect the "enemy" aircraft that would approach from the west at an unknown altitude.

For some minutes, the three flew on in a strange time warp of miles and darkness; while twelve thousand feet below them, the Pacific rolled by on an endless belt of tossing sea and cold hostility. In the ghost-green glow of the instrument panel, the radar scope was an engrossing eye searching the darkened miles ahead for targets. In his preoccupation with the search, Steve failed to detect the violent swing of the needle on the ammeter, indicating a direct short in the battery circuit. His first warning of impending disaster was the pungent smell of burning insulation permeating the cockpit. For an instant, there was renouncement, the refusal to believe what was happening to him, then in moments, the acceptance of reality, of life-threat, that sharpened his senses to needle-like focus. He stabbed at the bank of circuit breakers by his left knee and scanned the instrument panel, assessing in seconds the probability that there was no chance to save the airplane or perhaps even himself. By now, the red-hot wires in the engine's aft section had torched everything close to them. Oil residue had begun to burn, and the fire was irreversible.

Seconds later, the two wingmen saw the first yellow stabs of flame leaping back from the closed cowl flaps and realized that Dutton's Corsair was going down. In only seconds more, smoke, black and oil-laden now, was turning the cockpit into a suffocating trap.

Steve pushed the microphone button down and in a cold, even voice called, "Mayday, Mayday, she's burning; I'm going out."

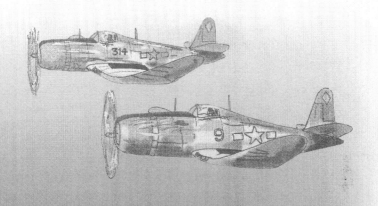

...the two wingmen saw the first yellow stabs
of flames leaping back from the closed cowl
flaps and realized Dutton's Corsair was going down.

Crash and Burn - Edward C. Larson, 2000

He jettisoned the cockpit canopy, released the seat and shoulder straps, and rolled the burning plane on its back. For an instant, he sensed his body clearing the cockpit. Then there came a staggering blow that broke his right leg and crushed his chest.

He had struck the plane's tail surface while ejecting, and he was now tumbling end over end through a black void.

Searching in disorientation for the D-ring on his chute harness, Steve half glimpsed the Corsair as it arched away to the west like a burning star — then the parachute opened, painfully twisting his fractured leg. Beneath the canopy, he descended through the immense darkness like a swinging pendulum, waiting for the sea. There was excruciating pain as his fractured leg struck the water and the instant sensation of cold as seawater saturated his flight jacket and coveralls.

The chute canopy had drifted free, and he pulled the inflations lanyards on his Mae West flight jacket. Only the left side inflated, the right cartridge hissed away emptily into the night, its chamber torn open by the collision with the tail surface.

Hanging by threads over Steve's right shoulder was the tiny, badly dented rescue light. Reaching with his left hand, he turned it on. Miraculously, it worked, giving a feeble glow in the universe of inky darkness. Floating crookedly in the heavy swell, he knew only pain, icy cold, and crushing silence.

Within seconds of Steve's message of disaster, the radar station had sent a message through the night to the communications center at Moffett Field, the Coast Guard Center at Monterrey, and to Officer Jack Buchholtz in his Santa Cruz police cruiser. Jack headed for the pay phone on the wharf.

It was eleven thirty when Paul Groszman's jangling telephone awakened him from a sound sleep. It was Jack with news of the crash, relaying a frantic call for help from the staff manning the radar station on the hill: they knew Paul's boat was still in the water.

For Groszman, there was no hesitation, only the recognition of a need, a galvanizing to action, and a determination to assist.

In a crush of seconds, a condensation of time, Paul, Jack, and Harlow Webber were aboard the *Tuna*. Groszman started the engine while Jack dropped the mooring line. A small whiteness wrinkled at her bow, and the boat was underway. Amazingly, it had taken only sixteen minutes. Among the three, there was a desperate sense of urgency and the commitment to provide at least that one slim chance of rescue—a search for a living needle in a haystack of monstrous proportions. In other places, men were jamming on flight jackets and buckling on Mae Wests as they ran toward waiting planes and rescue craft. It was a magnificent marshaling of forces intent on saving a life. Unfortunately, they were all too far away.

For Steve Dutton, the *Tuna* was the only game in town.

Tuna - Edward C. Larson, 2000

Her bow was now frothing white —

racing along her beam
...vanishing into the blackness of her stern.

With the Chrysler running full speed, the *Tuna* cleared the anchorage and began to respond to the heavy swell rolling in from the southwest. Her bow was now frothing white, racing along her beam and vanishing into the blackness of her stern. The two Corsairs from Dutton's flight, their fuel gauges sinking with the passing minutes, continued to orbit the crash site far to the northwest. Searching frantically at low altitude, they periodically dropped magnesium flares, turning the sea an electric blue. Groszman intuitively headed the *Tuna* away from the glare and toward the forbidding darkness, guessing that the westerly wind, tide, and swell would carry the drifting pilot far from the sinking wreckage of the downed fighter plane.

It was pitch black, and the schooner rolled beam to beam in the huge troughs as she clawed her way farther from the shore. To improve their night vision, Groszman had extinguished every light aboard save one, the anchor light, a small beacon at the top of the mast that would be visible to anyone in the water. It might provide that last increment of hope to the downed pilot.

Running at flank speed, the Tuna had covered perhaps six miles when Paul first heard the alien sound from the engine, a light, ominous knocking. Something was *wrong*. He flipped the instrument lights and swore as he saw the needle on the engine temperature gauge pegged at the top of the scale. A water line had collapsed under the pressure of their full-speed run and closed off the entire coolant system — the engine block was red hot! Paul cut the engine to an idle and shouted to Jack to take the wheel. Grabbing a teakettle from the galley stove, he ran aft, threw back the engine cover, and poured the contents into the empty radiator tank. Returning, he reached past the back of Jack's woolen fishing jacket, wet from the spray piling over the bow. Just as his hand was closing in on the throttle to kill the engine, he heard Webber scream, "*Jesus! He's out there! He's out there! I see his light!*"

Within seconds, Paul spotted the weak glow in the water, perhaps fifty yards off their starboard bow. Webber's voice cracked with emotion as he shouted twice into the darkness, "We're here! We're *here!*"

With an intensity of concentration beyond measure, they closed slowly on the faint light ahead, appearing and disappearing in the rolling swells. There was silence now among the three, each reveling in a fate that had led them to this small window of victory against odds that seemed impossible. From the beginning, Paul's logic had rebelled at the possibility of a successful outcome: too many variables in a game played out in the black of night on a stretch of trackless sea. But compassion had led them toward the darkness, and faith had held the course — about 120 degrees. The ultimate prize was now alongside their starboard quarter calling up to them in a hoarse voice, "I *knew* you'd find me. I saw your light."

In the heavy swell, it took the strength of all three men to lift the sodden pilot from the water. As they pulled him over the coarse wooden gunwale, he screamed in pain, and they immediately saw the badly broken right leg. He was only half conscious now from the effects of the fracture and hypothermia. They laid him carefully on a small bunk at the rear of the cabin, and Webber massaged his hands and arms as Buchholtz covered him with two old blankets. Paul turned the *Tuna* toward shore and with the engine noise worsening by the minute headed for the lights of the pier, six miles away.

As Webber continued rubbing life into the pilot's hands and arms, Dutton, dazed, stared at them with only partial recognition. Then in a whisper, he asked, "Hey Skipper, what in the hell's wrong with your engine?" He had been in the water exactly an hour and a half, about fifteen minutes short of death from exposure.

When they had started their journey back to shore, Groszman had radioed a message on the *Tuna*'s VHF set, and an ambulance and growing crowd awaited them as the schooner limped slowly to the landing. The old Chrysler had nearly breathed her last as they came alongside the dock, bearings melting into the oil pan, her shaft pounded flat. Dutton was carried by stretcher up the stairs from the landing; in minutes and with ambulance sirens screaming, he was whisked off to the Sister's Hospital a half mile away.

With news of the rescue, the circling Corsairs climbed to altitude and vanished on a course toward Moffett Field. A Coast Guard cutter dispatched from

Monterrey reversed direction fifteen miles out and returned to its base. Jack Buchholtz, shedding his wet fishing vest, walked to his police cruiser, slowly pulled away from the curb, and headed up toward Pacific Avenue.

The crowd was gone and the dark sea empty once more when Harlow Webber, last to leave, started up his aging pickup. With a last perfunctory goodnight to Paul, he drove away. As the aging Ford's taillights disappeared into the darkness, Paul leaned against the clapboard building and surveyed the stars and the flashing light from the one-mile buoy to the south. Across the cold distance, the low moan of the whistle spoke pleasantly in his mind. It had been a night of amazing good fortune. His boat, the last one in the water, had been ready. His course from anchorage had been one straight line, one predestined pathway from the wharf to an incredibly small pinpoint of life floating in a dark ocean. Finally, the old engine had lasted just long enough to bring them home.

A pocketful of miracles.

For some time, he stood there, a beer sign in the window flashing metallic blue on the planking at his slippered feet. The salt mist of morning dripped from the eaves of Malio Stagnaro's Fish Market and mixed with Paul Groszman's thoughts on the wonders of the night.

Paul Groszman, a man of substantial courage and sensitivity and a former Santa Cruz Harbor Commissioner, died on Christmas Day 1990, about a month after I wrote this story. He related the facts of the rescue to me while confined to bed due to severe calcification of his spine. In obvious pain, he was a kind and patient host as I sat by his bedside recording the details.

For as long as he was able, Paul operated his fishing boat. When he could no longer stand on deck, he accepted that decree of fate with characteristic graciousness.

LTJG Steve Dutton recovered from his injuries. Some weeks after the rescue, he was able to visit Paul and present him with a Navy check for a new engine for the *Tuna*. The trial of many years has grown too faint to determine Steve's present whereabouts. It is perhaps fair to surmise that this tale of courage and compassion has warmed his heart as it warmed Paul's heart through all the intervening years of his life.

Last Night - Edward C. Larson, 2017

last night

last night
i sat
and watched the world
creep
silently
to
bed

close its eyes
turn out its skies
and lay down
its head

perhaps I never noticed
it before
how earth puts out
its cat
and locks
its
door

I saw upon its sunset face
a touch of sorrow
and heard its "now i lay me down"
and other little child prayers
about tomorrow

With all the loveliness about
it's hard
to figure out
why sleeplessly she rolls from side to side
and disarrays her counterpane
of eventide
yet finds it quite impossible
to sleep
and spends full half the night
just
counting
sheep

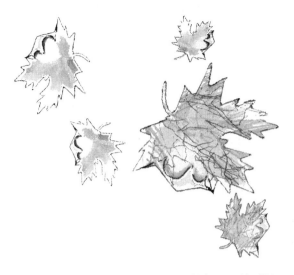

Maple Leaves - Edward C. Larson, 2017

leaves

A new November came short days ago.
She danced across the quarter notes of autumn,
like clustered snow geese,
riding a wind
toward the promise of a softer winter.

As we walk,
brown leaves,
silent harbingers of December and beyond,
float softly down
to lie in state
beside a sea
that seems eternally ours to share.

IV

Autumn: the hush before winter
- French proverb

Clean Up - Edward C. Larson, 2017

acknowledgments

In several passages of this book, I have made reference to falling leaves and the autumns of yesterday.

For ninety-plus years, I have been scribbling down poems and stuff on random sticky notes and brown paper bags. The pathway of my life was strewn with the litter of my living. Fractured bits of verse and worse had been carelessly mixed in with the curled, dry, fallen leaves of a lifetime of autumns past. The pathway behind me was a mess. A cleanup crew was desperately needed.

Sheila Setter, who built this book from scraps of frozen prose and Iambic "pent-amateur," told me long ago it was time for me to clean up my act.

As usual, she was right.

Through the years, I have assembled about me a coterie of lady elves willing to work at difficult tasks for absolutely no remuneration whatsoever. In truth, these are real people but infused with the DNA of those tiny beings who often float about the petals of "meadow flowers" blooming in late spring and early summer.

These denizens of daffodils and sunlit daisies were called upon to help and readily accepted the task of cleaning up after me, gathering up that which I had carelessly cast aside through the journey of my years. Under the capable tutelage of Sheila Setter (now designated as "elf alpha"), this willing crew broomed, raked, and shoveled the litany of dry sketches and misguided prose into a neat pile, which now constitutes the contents of this book.

My daffodil denizens, who worked so assiduously, have earned a respite and now return to the flowers and meadows of late summer. Thankfully, they have forever split from the male counterparts of their species, who live in perpetual dampness beneath old stone bridges, shunning work and drinking heavy ales from goatskin bota bags. My deepest love and thanks go to each of these women for their diligence and devotion on my behalf—a treasured gift indeed.

As for me, I shall continue my way down the errant path they have prepared for me. My reprehensible practice of scattering misguided scraps of prose will occur only when absolutely necessary for the maintenance of my ongoing peace of mind.

Tina Larson

Toward the end of our book, Elf Delta, in the personage of my beloved daughter, Tina Larson, departed on an eternal journey to sunlit meadows and fields just beyond our reach. A devoted "leaf sweeper," she was ever-present to accept the tasks that seemed to fill the days we spent together.

In a co-dependency, we shared the physical inconveniences that were our constant companions. We fought and laughed through days that should have numbered far more than they did.

Tina, your energy and efforts are the fabric of these pages. God bless you. Enjoy tending your new gardens as much as you enjoyed tending the one we shared.

Remember Bon's spirit still roams the old pasture by our house. Catch him up, throw on his bridle, and ride the river with the wind. All my love is with you.

Jeanne Marcucci

Elf Gamma masquerades as Jeanne Marcucci— ex-elementary schoolteacher and *bon vivant*. She types with the speed of light, "loves the flowers of summer," and rakes leaves with indescribable vigor.

Given to lengthy monologues on history and the arts, Jeanne has served as proofreader, savage critic, gadfly, and revered companion.

Jeanne Ann, your support, laughter, and enthusiasm make life worthwhile. Thank you for sharing with me the books we have read and the meadows we have walked together.

Patricia D. Richards

Elf Beta, aka Patricia Richards, is a seasoned traveler; and following graduation from the University of Washington,

she has traveled almost constantly, adding two master's degrees in her journeys. An early interest in cameras morphed into a passion for photography, which she has pursued her entire life.

Early on, Patty shunned color, concentrating on the creation of magnificent black and white photographs, which project not only a visual mastery but also a profound sense of spirituality, sensitivity, and the emotional impact of the scene or subject involved. Such intuition has characterized her work since the beginning.

On her first visit to Cuba, she realized that color was a mandate. In nine subsequent journeys to the island, she has produced a wealth of hauntingly beautiful visual statements that shout of Cuban culture and the romantic worth of its people, so long estranged from the citizenry of our shores.

As testimony to the appeal of her work, Patty's photographs can be seen at The Smithsonian, the San Francisco Museum of Modern Art, and in the holdings of many public and private collections around the world. She is currently a professor of photography at Tarrant County College in North Texas.

I am deeply proud and privileged to have examples of Patty's work enlighten the pages of this book, just as they have enlightened my years.

Sheila Setter

Please believe me when I tell you that Elf Alpha is not of our planet. Her true being exists in the world of books some light-years away from our earthly domain.

Only on rare occasions does she assume her humanoid manifestation as Sheila Setter, mild-mannered homemaker of Austin, Texas.

Sheila can often be found in the lovely home she shares with beloved husband Greg, equally beloved daughter Amy, and small wirehaired terrier, Tinker Bell, also beloved and an experienced canine interplanetary traveler.

A graduate of the University of Texas at Dallas, she holds a degree in visual arts and performance and has served the publishing business in myriad roles for the past thirty years. Constantly flitting from flower to flower, she has done it all: copy editing, technical writing and editing, graphics creation, book design, and more. Her nonearthly talents include genius stature in computer technology and a total devotion to her Church, her family, and to a litany of friends and admirers. I am deeply grateful and humbled that she has been the main leaf sweeper in the creation of this little book.

In a beautiful "ping-pong game" of words and creative design, Sheila and I have, for years, swung the paddles of collaborative joy and the blatant "high" of literary adventure.

We do books for fun, and the pervasive spirit and encouragement of my dear friend and partner makes nailing the words together a personally unforgettable and unique experience in my life.

Thank you for that, Elf Alpha!

It's your serve!

One Hundred and Thirteen Miles - Edward C. Larson, 2017

one hundred & thirteen miles

One hundred and thirteen miles southwest
of Bonner's Ferry, Idaho...

Eddie-Boy gets carsick.
Eddie-Boy throws up on Uncle Chuck.
Uncle Chuck smacks Eddie-Boy.
Eddie-Boy cries.
Violet smacks Uncle Chuck.
Left-rear tire blows out.
No spare.

Grandpa shouts, "*Sonofabitch!*"

...It's starting to rain.

No one knows
if it was the new car...

or if the
boys

just felt like

posing

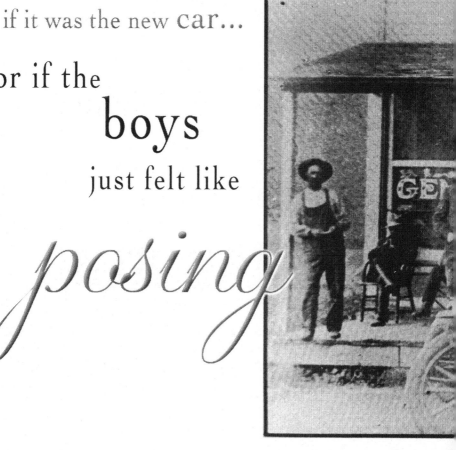

Charlie Rehm behind the Wheel - Absarokee, Montana, 1908
from the Author's Collection

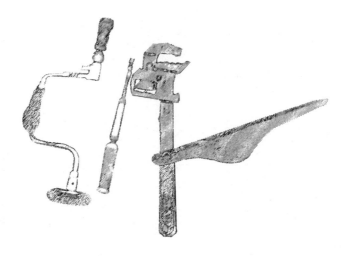

Tools of the Trade - Edward C. Larson, 2005

list of illustrations/credits

Bibliography

Larson, Edward C. *Spear-Carrier in a Backwater War.*
    Santa Cruz, CA: Fly by Night Graphics, 2014.

———— *Pebbles from a Favored Shore.* Santa Cruz, CA:
    Fly by Night Graphics, 2005.

_____ *Gaff-Rigged Remembrance: Writings from the Santa Cruz Harbor.* Santa Cruz, CA: Fly by Night Graphics, 2000.

_____ *Spring Tides: Memories of Alaskan Towboats.* Santa Cruz, CA: Fly by Night Graphics, 1996.

Larson, Edward C., and Les Burpo. *Some Things We Lived With.* (Santa Cruz, CA: Fly by Night Graphics, 1972).

Art Credits

Richards, Patricia D. *Edward C. Larson,* 2014.

_____ *Grandpa's Barn II,* 2000.

_____ *The Fishtail General Store,* 1992.

_____ *Grandpa's Barn,* 1992.

_____ *Along the Stillwater,* 1992.

The narratives in this book are set in Cochin LT Pro, a typeface drawn by French designer Georges Peignot (1872–1914) and based on copper engravings of the 18th century.

Poetry is set in Malgun Gothic.

Made in the USA
San Bernardino, CA
03 January 2018